# FARM WORKSHOP AND MAINTENANCE

The book of the **Farmers Weekly** series

**SECOND EDITION**
**Revisions by Bill Butterworth**

**GRANADA**
London Toronto Sydney New York

Granada Publishing Limited — Technical Books Division
Frogmore, St Albans, Herts AL2 2NF
and
3 Upper James Street, London W1R 4BP
866 United Nations Plaza, New York, NY 10017, USA
117 York Street, Sydney, NSW 2000, Australia
100 Skyway Avenue, Rexdale, Ontario M9W 3A6, Canada
PO Box 84165, Greenside, 2034 Johannesburg, South Africa
CML Centre, Queen & Wyndham, Auckland 1, New Zealand

ISBN 0 246 11358 8

First published in Great Britain 1972 by Crosby Lockwood Staples
Reprinted 1978
Second edition 1979 (original ISBN 0 258 97133 9)
Reprinted 1980 by Granada Publishing Limited — Technical Books Division

Printed in Great Britain by Fletcher & Son Ltd., Norwich

Granada ®
Granada Publishing ®

# INTRODUCTION

Farmers are great "do-it-yourself" men. They have to be. Few of them can afford a resident, full-time mechanic. And when farm machinery breaks down, it must be back in action without delay, for in a difficult season the ability to get on quickly with the sowing or harvesting can mean the difference between profit or loss on a particular crop.

But a mere handiness with tools is not enough. Modern farm tackle is complicated and precision-built; it demands sympathetic, skilled adjustment and repair with precision tools by people who understand how it works. We at *Farmers Weekly*, with our own six farms, know how important such skill and understanding are. That is why we have produced the weekly series of "Workshop" articles on which this book is based.

TRAVERS LEGGE.
Editor, *Farmers Weekly.*

# METRICATION NOTE

Like the rod, pole or perch (or, for that matter, the bushel), there are many imperial measures which will stay in common use in farming for many years to come. Indeed, one researcher identified 214 different thread types in use throughout the world. Even though the U.K. is officially fully metricated, many engineering tools such as hammers are still produced and sold in the imperial sizes and will continue so for some years. Yet metric units will become increasingly used. With this background, this book has been largely based on metric units so that the new measures can be clearly understood. Imperial units have been retained, however, where relevant and useful, in recognition that many machines that will need farm workshop attention will, inevitably, be old but useful.

# CONTENTS

# IN THE FIELD AND AT THE BENCH

## A NOTEBOOK FOR THE FARM MECHANIC

### Tool-kit or telephone?

A man good with his hands can make repairs or adjustments when the need is pointed out, but may sooner or later ask himself whether major overhauls should be attempted in the farm workshop or limited to general upkeep and routine maintenance. The ability of the individual is critical. A little knowledge is as dangerous here as around any other part of the farm.

Failure of starter motors, generators and other proprietary items causes no major problems in this age of replacement units. Usually the remedy is simply a matter of obtaining the necessary part and fitting it.

The time to start thinking about drawing the line comes when complete engine, transmission, or fuel injection equipment overhauls are thought to be necessary. Before having a go at this sort of job call in the dealer and get his advice. It may be that the symptoms have been incorrectly diagnosed. For example, loss of engine power may be the result of stuck, worn rings, the injection pump not functioning normally or something as simple as an obstructed air supply.

### Judgement and costs

Special tools and equipment required for carrying out major repairs on a small number of tractors are often too costly for the amount of work to be done. Some farmers with large well equipped workshops have found this out the hard way and have reverted to employing local dealers to do major overhauls. In any case the time spent on this sort of workshop job should never be at the expense of more important jobs outside, especially when the weather is right.

### Clean up campaign

Farm dirt and the precision parts that go into an increasing number of farm machines nowadays do not go well together. Makers of electronic components who thought they were supplying for an elementary process by their standards, have had to think twice when faced with the combination of dirt and damp under which their units were expected to function on farms. Now they seal them or encase them in plastic. A replacement part is simply plugged in.

Engine manufacturers have lived with the problem for much longer and have developed their own ways of keeping dirt at bay. But filters still rely on basic common sense and co-operation from the user if all is to go well.

A diesel engine contains precision parts which tolerate far less 'dirt' than many people realise if they are to run efficiently. It is difficult enough to think in terms of fractions of a millimetre and a micron may not seem worth bothering about. Yet at this size a particle of something as fine as cigarette ash or lamp black relatively seems like half a brick to the finely ground mating surfaces of a diesel tractor's pump and injectors and can soon start wearing away these surfaces. So we start our look at what makes the tractor 'tick' with the fuel system (page 52).

### Look at the book

A browse through the instruction book is essential before putting any piece of equipment to work. This may sound elementary, but it is often ignored particularly if the machine is a direct replacement of a familiar model.

What is usually forgotten is that the machine is almost certain to have been modified since the original and operating and maintenance procedures may also have changed.

Many manufacturers spend a lot of time and money on their instruction books; others make do with a printed sheet of so-called instructions.

Good though the former editions may be there is always room for improvement, usually in simplifying explanations still further. Familiarity is a dangerous thing for instruction book scribes, the more they know about a machine the more difficult it is to look at the subject through the eyes of the man who has just bought one and knows nothing about it.

### Comprehension test

There is much to be said for the technique of the executive in one company, who admitted that he knew little about the technical side of the equipment he sold but insisted that he saw all publicity and instruction material before it was published. 'If I can understand it anyone can,' he said.

To the firms which issue the other sort of instructions the message is clear. Apart from a moral duty to make sure that whoever buys the machine knows how to work it, the poor farmer can hardly be blamed if he does the wrong thing.

Happily, more and more firms are becoming conscious of the need to provide the right sort of operating instructions, with useful tips on how to get the best out of the particular piece of equipment in the varying conditions under which it will be expected to work.

Our idea is to aid and abet the dissemination of information. Perhaps the time will come when such a bridge between maker and user will not be necessary. Until then, we hope to help you to get more and better work done with fewer frustrations.

### Calibration problem

Following up the instruction theme, the calibrating of fertiliser spreaders is a case where the farmer needs more help. In these days of increasingly concentrated fertilisers, the misses and double doses are embarrassingly evident, quite apart from the financial waste.

Many spreader makers issue clear setting instructions, but farmers ought to be able to calibrate for themselves, especially as a check after a year or two of work may be desirable to allow for normal wear.

Calibrating a spinning disc spreader to find its spread pattern across the direction of travel means putting down a line of boxes, driving over them, and tipping the results into a row of tubes which then show the 'hump' visually so that the necessary overlap can be calculated.

Demonstrations of such calibrations have shown it is necessary on some machines to cut down the makers' recommended bout width by up to a metre to get even coverage.

### Some other way?

The only ways to calibrate for application rate per hectare are to sow a measured area and calculate, or put 50 kg in the hopper, run it out, then measure up and work out the calibration. This assumes that the maker's bout width measurements are correct.

There must be a more simple universal way apart from the one or two specialist versions developed for individual machines by more enlightened manufacturers.

The need for accurate calibrating becomes more necessary as fertiliser application rates and prices increase. In fact, the 'big three' fertiliser companies do offer a spreader clinic service to make sure that their regular customers have machines that use their fertilisers efficiently.

### Colour guide to lubrication

Locating the position of grease nipples on new machines can, even with the help of an instruction manual, be like looking for a needle in a hay-stack. And remembering when they should be greased can test the best memory.

The time taken for maintenance has been reduced considerably by the introduction of sealed bearings, but some bearings still require the attention of the grease-gun. It is not always lack of lubrication that causes failures; too much grease will in many cases lead to just as much trouble.

A simple system, which helps in ensuring the correct greasing period, helps in locating the nipples and saves having to wander around with manual in one hand and grease-gun in the other, is to identify nipples with different coloured paint. Paint them in accordance with the maintenance schedule, one colour for those needing four-hourly attention, another colour for eight-hourly, and so on.

This will cut the time spent on maintenance and help safeguard against missing an important grease point. Nipples can be seen at a glance through the colour coding when they need attention.

Much time and grease can be wasted through blocked or damaged nipples. To overcome this in the field place a piece of rag between the nipple and the grease-gun nozzle. It will act as a seal and give a greater pumping pressure. If this method fails a new nipple will have to be fitted.

### The arch enemy

Rust is an arch enemy of the farmer. It attacks and eats into all ferrous metals and if not checked, will quickly reduce the resale value of a piece of tackle considerably. However, most metal surfaces can be treated to prevent corrosion by painting, galvanising or applying one of the many preparations on the market.

Nevertheless, few machines have nuts and bolts which have had their threads so treated, and the old problem of seized nuts is still with us. Do not resort to fitting a length of pipe on to the spanner, or reaching for the hammer and chisel, there are a number of remedies for releasing seized nuts.

## 'First aid' on stubborn nuts

Penetrating oils, obtainable in aerosol tins, have rust solvents and lubricants as part of their ingredients, and if given time to work on the rust will usually do the job. However, it is not always to hand when needed in the field. A drop of diesel or TVO in this instant will deal with rust much more quickly than ordinary oil because being thinner, it gets further into the threads.

A gentle tap on opposing flats with two hammers will usually release a stubborn nut. This breaks the rust crust between the threads and allows the oil to penetrate.

## Oiling roller chains

Under some abrasive conditions chains will last longer without lubrication though the oiling of roller chains is usually advisable to increase their life. Periodic dipping in an oil-bath is recognised as the best method, but if this is inconvenient brush on or squirt the oil straight from the can.

Brown or black discoloration or red oxide deposits on the links are warnings of insufficient lubrication, which will also show up as different rates of wear in different areas of the same chain.

If a chain is removed from any assembly which involves timing make sure the timing marks on the sprocket are in the right place before it is replaced.

For some jobs double sprocket drives are used and teeth must be in line. Otherwise jerky drives, sprocket wear and chain failure will result.

Sometimes 'skip tooth' sprockets, so called because every other tooth is missing, are used to prevent the crop building up between the chain links and the teeth. On driving elevator chains it is important that slats or flights in the chain are in mesh with the skipped tooth.

The right amount of sag in a chain is important. A chain allowed to whip because it is too slack puts tremendous shock loading through the pins and bushings. On the other hand a chain adjusted too tightly will prevent oil penetrating between the pins and bushings and result in rapid wear.

Generally, chain sag should be 3 per cent of the slack length. For example, 50 cm of slack chain calls for 15 mm sag.

## Safety—inside and out

A discussion on farm machinery is incomplete without some mention of safety. Though some may think that the safety message is rammed too hard down our throats these days, there can be no argument about the figures, over 100 killed on farms annually, nearly one quarter of them children, in the worst year ever. In fact 170 children have been killed on farms in the past 10 years and nearly half these were under eight. On this score there can never be enough talk about safety. *

Though the regulations forbid a child under 13 to drive or ride on a tractor, and driving some modern tractor and implement combinations is beyond their ability one still sees them trying.

Constant vigilance to prevent the grisly record from growing is needed in the implement shed or workshop as well as in the fields. Tackle parts removed for repair are often propped up in the most dangerous way. One sees people relying upon a comparatively flimsy jack and no secondary support to prevent a heavy implement from crushing them if something should go wrong. It all boils down to common sense, but too often this is impaired by familiarity and the contempt which accompanies it.

*Guide to Safety in Agriculture
International Labour Office, Geneva, 1970

# BEGINNING AT THE WORKBENCH

## HINTS TO SAVE KNUCKLES, TEMPER, TIME AND MONEY

Today, when profit margins can be wiped out merely by failure to get a broken machine quickly back into action, the man whose farm 'workshop' is merely an old 'ammo' box of assorted tools is putting himself and his farming at hazard. Even if facilities consist of no more than a permanent workbench which provides an ordered place for tools and accessories there is already some guarantee against frustration and despair—as will be testified by anyone who has torn his knuckles and mangled components when trying to repair a machine with the wrong tools because the right ones cannot be found.

The bench is the starting point and whether it is a highly sophisticated, bought-in affair or home-made from odd bits of timber, it should be solid and roomy. A metal top is to be preferred and is not such an extravagance as it sounds; wooden ones can become oil sodden and a metal sheet preserves a smooth, hard-wearing working surface.

Site the bench under a window if possible and in any case make sure it has adequate artificial light. Racks full of spring clips or trays, divided shelves or other systems to keep things together, should be close by. A solid old sideboard picked up from a farm sale can serve as a crude but use-

The wrong type of bolt: the square shank in the round hole anchoring the vice gives little support and the vice will soon work loose. Over-tightening could result in the flange breaking off.

ful workbench with a sheet of metal added; old household chests of drawers can make splendid tool cabinets.

Simple wooden racks holding oil tins cut in half provide cheap but efficient storage for spares. The grooves in strips of corrugated sheet make ideal compartments for keeping small components apart; the axle and discs from an old set of disc harrows with a tripod welded on one end allows it to stand upright and form a 'cakestand' type of receptacle for nuts and bolts. These are a few of the ingenious ideas that have served well in farm workshops and have cost virtually nothing. We shall be discussing them in detail later. The main aim should be to create order out of chaos and keep it that way.

The workbench must have a vice—two if finances will stretch to it. A hefty one is needed for the big items and a smaller one for the more delicate parts.

The bench must be big and strong enough to withstand rough treatment. The more working space available the better. Small benches soon become cluttered up with bits and pieces of machinery often to the point where there is no room for tools. It is no major operation to make a good large substantial work-top so the vice has the top of the jaws equal to the height of the worker's elbow from the ground, with the arm bent.

## CHOOSING A VICE

It pays to have a vice that will stand up to such jobs as bending or riveting.

There are are two main types, the leg-vice and the parallel-jaw vice. The leg vice has the reputation of being exceptionally strong. Blacksmiths prefer it; it is ideal for gripping metal which needs to be chipped, hammered or bent rather than the more delicate job.

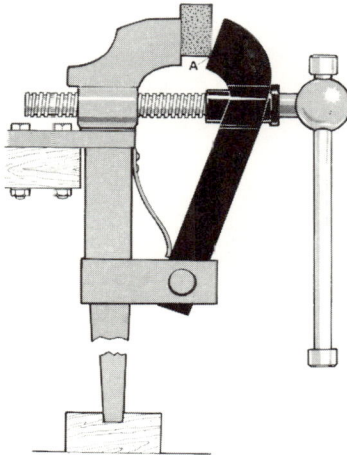

A leg-vice. The leg may be let into the floor or supported on a wooden block firmly attached to the floor. It is more rigid than types fixed only to bench top.

It has one big disadvantage; the jaws do not meet squarely due to the movable jaw being pivoted halfway down the support leg (*See A in the drawing*). This makes the jaw move through an arc and it is parallel to the fixed jaw only when the vice is closed. To hold work securely it is often necessary to grip it very tightly, which can result in distortion.

The parallel-jaw vice was designed to overcome this problem and is now the most popular vice in engineering. Many different makes and types are available, but for all-round farm workshop a **12 cm** model which opens to **15 cm**, with renewable jaw-plates without quick release arrangement, will cope with the majority of work.

A quick-release mechanism saves time but this type of vice does not stand up to hard work as well as a fixed-nut type.

It is worth paying a little extra for a swivel base vice. When dealing with large, awkward pieces of tackle or long lengths of pipe it is a great help to be able to position the vice so that the work does not foul a bench or wall. It may be swivelled in a complete circle and locked in any position.

The jaws of the vice are made from cast steel and serrated like a file. To prevent damage to soft metal or to bolt threads it is worth while making a set of protection pads for the jaws. Lead, hard wood or fibre are ideal materials.

Keep the vice in good working order. Check that the jaw-plates are tight and renew the set screws if they are worn. Clean the tightening screw threads occasionally to remove from filings and dirt. Care should be taken not to over-oil the threads.

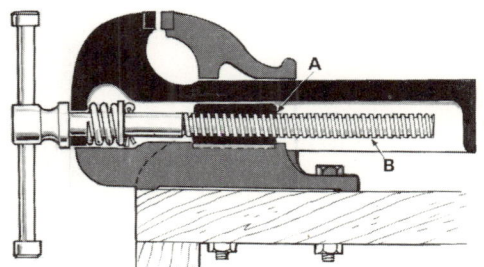

A fixed nut parallel-jaw vice—the combination of the nut A being more or less part of the body and the square threaded screw B tends to make it much stronger than quick release vices.

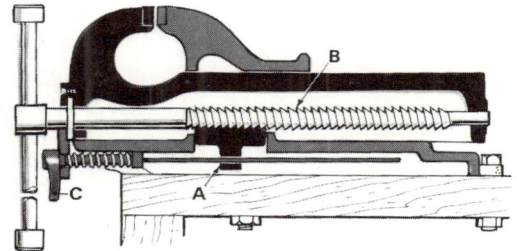

Parallel-jaw vice with quick release arrangement. By pressing lever C the half nut A, which may be renewed when worn, is disengaged from the buttress threaded screw B.

## THE TOOL KIT

There is a lot to be said for gradually building up a tool kit rather than buying it all at once. The contents depend largely on what equipment is to be maintained and how much do-it-yourself work is likely to be attempted. There are, however, a few basic essentials, such as spanners, hammers, pliers and screwdrivers, with spanners coming at the top of the list.

A golden rule in engineering is always to use the correct tool for the job in hand and this applies especially to spanners. Adjustable and Stilson wrenches are fine when used in the right application, but all too often small bolts and studs are sheared off because an adjustable spanner is used instead of a small ring one. Also there is nothing more annoying than coming across a metric nut in an awkward corner and finding that the only spanners available are Whitworth.

So before buying tools, take stock of the types of nuts used in your range of tackle. They might be BSW (British Standard Whitworth), American SAE (Society of Automotive Engineers), or Metric. American SAE measurements are made across the nut and not across the bolt, which the nut is to fit, as for other types. This measurement is known as AF (across the flats) and is referred to much more than SAE.

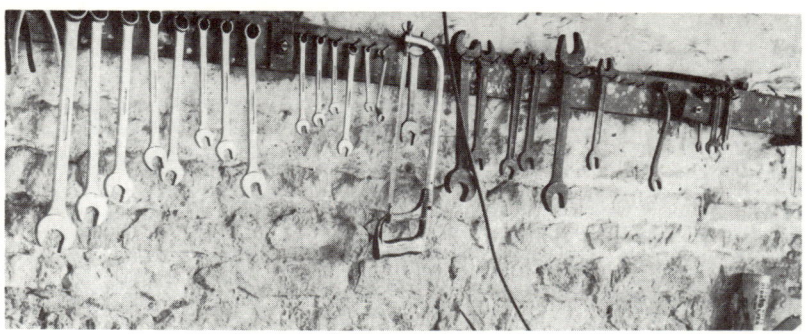

A few nails in a batten fixed to the wall provides an excellent easy-to-reach tool rack

A set of sockets including ratchet, long and short extensions, flexible coupling and both AF and metric sizes is a portable tool box within itself.

The quickest way to ruin an adjustable wrench (below): the small jaw is taking most of the strain.

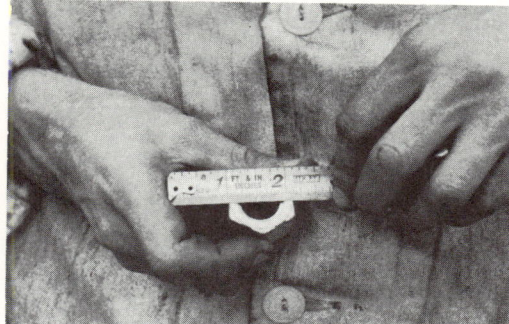

Measuring across the flats of $1\frac{1}{8}$in AF nut

Leave the adjustable wrench in the tool box when doing jobs like this; use the correct size open-ended or ring spanner.

This method of increasing leverage may help to slacken a stubborn nut but it won't do the spanners any good.

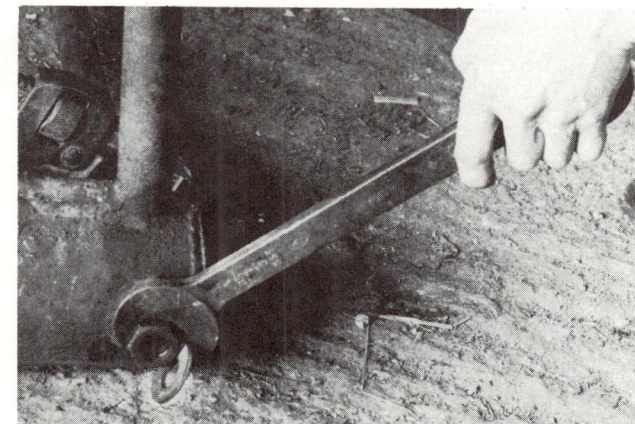

A washer makes a good packing piece when the only available spanner is too big.

Open-ended spanners should be bought in complete sets rather than individually because it is always the one missing that is wanted in a hurry. Basic essentials should include BSW $\frac{1}{8}$ to $\frac{3}{4}$in, AF $\frac{5}{16}$ to 1in and metric 10—20mm. Make sure the sizes overlap, for example, $\frac{1}{8} - \frac{1}{4}$, $\frac{1}{4} - \frac{5}{16}$, $\frac{5}{16} - \frac{3}{8}$ and so on. Two spanners of the same size are often needed when releasing or retightening locking nuts.

## CARE OF SPANNERS

The jaws of a normal double open-ended spanner are set at an angle of 30 deg to the handle, which is sufficient for most jobs, but there are, however, some which have jaws set at 75 deg or even 85 deg. These types are called obstruction spanners and are used where it is impossible to get a 30 deg spanner on to a nut. Obstruction spanners are a luxury and would be seldom used in the farm workshop.

It is much better to buy a few double-ended ring spanners. They have 12 corners or points on the inner edge of the ring and can, therefore, be fitted to a nut in 12 different positions. A full set is unnecessary. Every alternate one in the range will be sufficient. Gaps can be filled by buying a box of sockets including both AF and metric sizes.

Spanners must not be abused as makeshift hammers and levers. Even though they are made from hardened tough steel, the jaws will eventually extend and start slipping off nuts. Fitting the

A sheet of 1.6 mm mild steel nailed and screwed to the top of a rough oil impregnated wooden bench will give it a new lease of life and provide a smooth, easy-to-keep-clean work surface. (Right) A mound of concrete at the bottom of each leg is ideal for keeping the bench rigid.

spanner to a nut in the wrong way may also lead to damaged jaws. The correct method is with the smaller jaw arm towards the line of pull—which leaves the larger jaw to take the main strain.

Placing a length of pipe over the end of a spanner to obtain greater leverage is safe only with large bolts.

Undue pressure on small sizes will strip threads or shear bolts. The length of a spanner is designed to give adequate leverage for an average handpull.

The hammer gets more than its fair share of work on most farms and is more often than not required in two places at the same time. So it is wise to have, in addition to the usual 14lb sledge, a couple of 2lb and 1lb ball-pein hammers for general work and riveting.

A hammer with a copper or hide face will be useful, especially when removing bearing and brass bushings.

The tool boxes fitted to tractors and implements are often so small that the farmer has to make up his own portable tool box. Carrying the odd spanner and hammer is not enough for dealing with the more complicated tackle, such as combines and balers. A comprehensive selection of gear is required with the addition of a few bolts, nuts, washers, cotterpins and the odd part that is known to be suspect. An emergency supply of baler shear bolts can save a journey back to the workshop.

Tools from a portable kit will be used for ordinary work in the workshop, but a rule should be made that they are always replaced after use. To avoid searching for tools in the bottom of the box, fit it out with clips or divide it into compartments to hold the spanners and the smaller items.

## SOCKET SPANNERS

Socket spanners, tubular and made of alloy steel, are usually 12-pointed each side allowing a nut to be moved 30 deg. The advantages are that there is little risk of damage to either nut or hands and access to a nut in a restricted position is easier. The spanners can also be used on square nuts without damaging the nut or slipping.

Sockets can be bought in metric sets but only the sockets themselves are in metric sizes. The fittings and drive bars (the piece that fits into the back of the socket) are still made in imperial sizes.

The driving bar can be $\frac{3}{8}$in, $\frac{1}{2}$in or $\frac{3}{4}$in square. If the spanners are to be used on heavy work, such as crawler track adjustment or undoing wheel nuts, buy a set with $\frac{3}{4}$in drive bar. Half-inch drive will be sufficient for normal workshop use.

Buy the best set you can afford; they are not cheap but they will last for years and the bigger the set the more accessories you get. Accessories in more expensive sets include the speed brace for tightening and undoing nuts quickly, a ratchet handle for the same purpose in restricted access, the universal joint for awkward nuts and bolts, and a set of long and short extension bars.

Extra long sockets, for nuts and bolts in recesses or where a nut is on a long threaded bar, screwdrivers and sparking plug spanners can also be bought.

If you have many Continental machines on the farm, and with more and more manufacturers turning to metric hardware, a metric set will be the best buy.

Maintenance is minimal; wipe down with an oily rag after use and put a drop of thin oil on the ratchet occasionally.

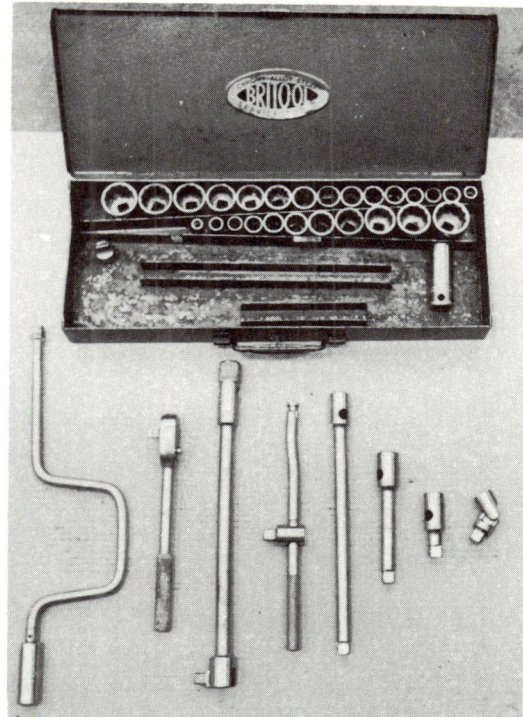

This set costs about £40.

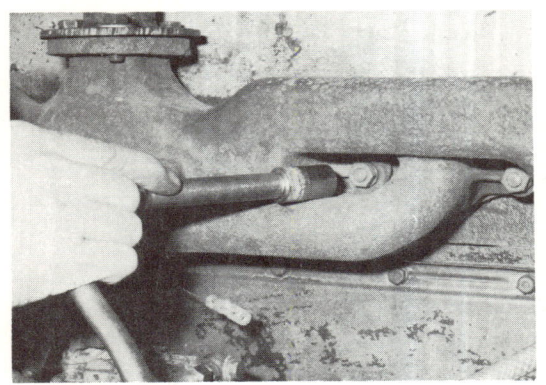

A tough problem solved with a socket spanner.

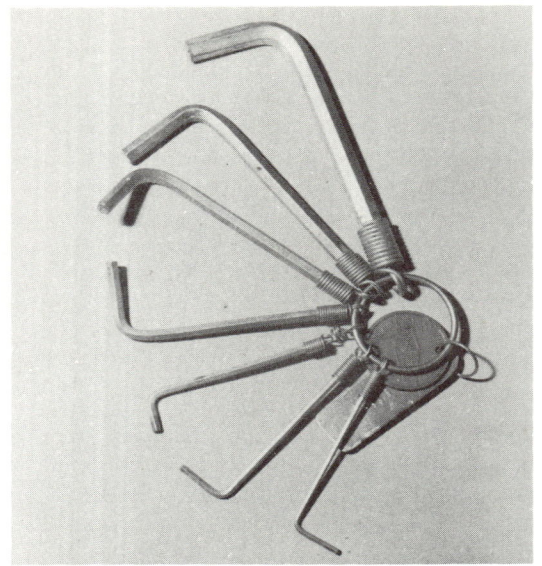

A set of Allen keys is not expensive.

Grub screws usually need Allen keys.

## THE RIGHT KEYS FOR GRUB SCREWS

A set of Allen keys is a useful accessory in a workshop. The keys are made of tool steel, are hexagonal in section, and have a right-angled bend in them. The bend allows either end of the key to be used while the other is gripped to exert twist.

On farm machinery Allen keys are mainly used on small grub screws to hold bearings, lock-collars and baler knives in position. There are some screws with hexagonal recesses in the head but they are uncommon in agriculture.

Most common sizes of key are from $\frac{1}{8}$ in to $\frac{1}{2}$ in or from 3 mm to 12 mm and a set to fit in this range will be adequate for the farm workshop. Bigger keys can be bought separately.

Measurements are taken across the flats of the hexagonal. Always use the correct size of key as it is easy to damage the flats of a grub-screw, particularly the small ones.

A set of Whitworth, AF or metric sizes is not expensive and they can be bought attached to a key-ring.

## PLIERS

When selecting the smaller hand tool such as pliers it pays to shop around a bit to hunt out the types which have more than one use, such as as a pair of square-nosed pliers with side wire cutters and insulated handles. Some incorporate a stronger cutting device either side of the hinge rivet and these are usually capable of hand ing wire up to 3 mm thick. They are the ideal tool for trimming and cutting split pins to length.

Here are a few of the many shapes and sizes of pliers available.

Vice grips with wire cutters. It is best to buy a large pair of these. They can be used as pipe grips as well as for clamping metal for cutting, welding or drilling.

Multi-purpose pliers incorporating hammer head, wire cutters, staple remover, square and round gripping jaws and nail remover. An ideal tool for fencing jobs and in the workshop.

Square-nosed straight jaw pliers with insulated handles. The jaws are slightly tapered towards their ends and have small serrations to give a firm grip. Others are; round-nosed pliers, square-nosed pliers with straight and curved jaws, long-nosed pliers, pointed-nose pliers (handy for holding small nails or rivets in position), heavy duty long-nosed pliers with wire cutters, external circlip pliers with right angle points, and curved long-nosed pliers.

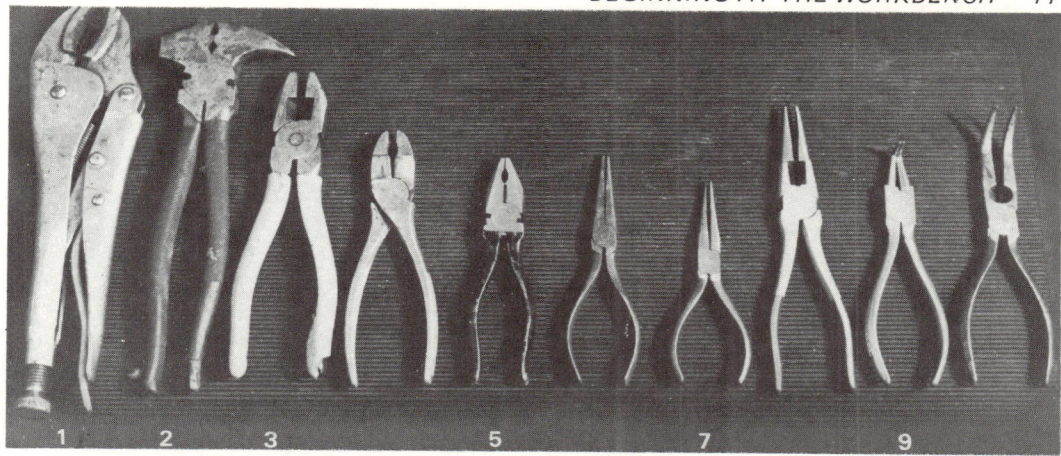

The numbered pliers are the types most suitable for farm workshop use.

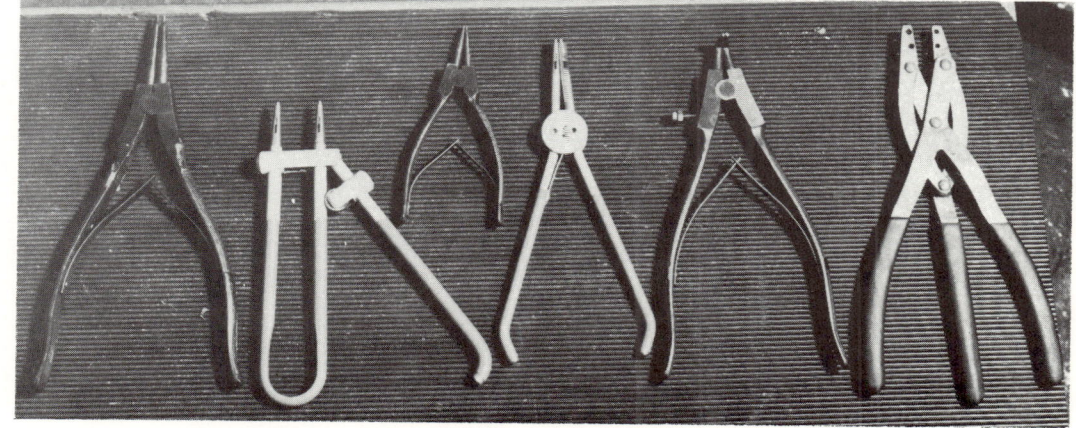

A few types of circlip pliers. The pair on the right are supplied with interchangeable tips.

## DRILLS

Blunt drills cause problems and breakages, so accurate sharpening is vital. There are two main points to watch.

The cutting lips must have sufficient clearance behind the cutting edges to give the drill bite. The correct amount is about 12 deg. (See Fig 1).

Fig. 1

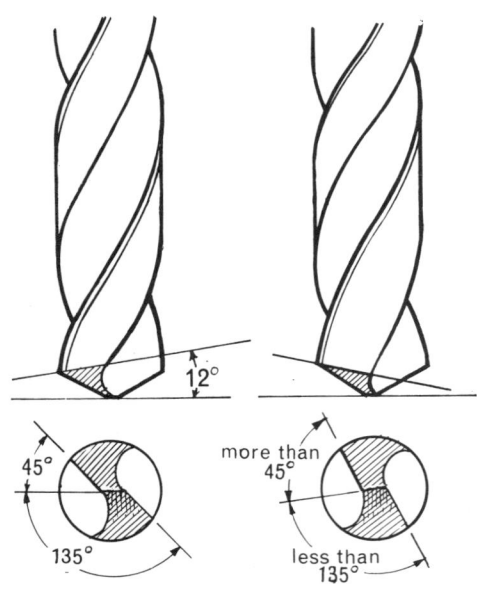

CORRECT        INCORRECT

The cutting edges must be the same length and make exactly the same angle with the centre line of the drill. The angle for general work is 50 to 60 deg.

Cutting lips need enough clearance for the drill to bite into the metal, otherwise it will screech, vibrate and overheat. But if there is too much it will feed too fast, taking large bites at each revolution and increasing the possibility of breakage.

Clearance may be checked by standing the drill on a level surface, point down, alongside a steel rule and then turning it slowly. If the heel of the cutting edge is slightly higher than the front of the cutting edge and the angle is about 12 deg, clearance is correct. (See Fig. 2).

Fig. 2

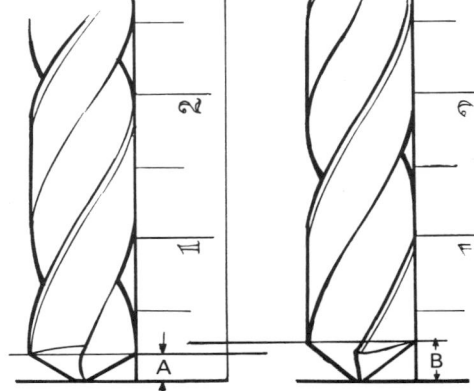

Checking lip clearance angle by steel rule. B should be slightly greater than A after rotating the drill.

Drills need different cutting angles for different metals. For all-round mild steel drilling 59 to 60 deg is best; for cast iron 50 deg and for brass 45 degrees. Hard steels are difficult to drill but by grinding the cutting angle flatter to 75 deg, the job may be made easier.

If both cutting edges are not the same length the point of the drill is not central. It will bore an oversized hole and transfer most of the work on to one edge causing it to become blunt more quickly. If the lips are not ground to the correct angle the drill will be either too blunt or too pointed.

To check the angle, put two bright steel hexagon nuts together. The adjacent pair of flats give an angle of 120 degrees thus making it possible to check both edges together (see photograph).

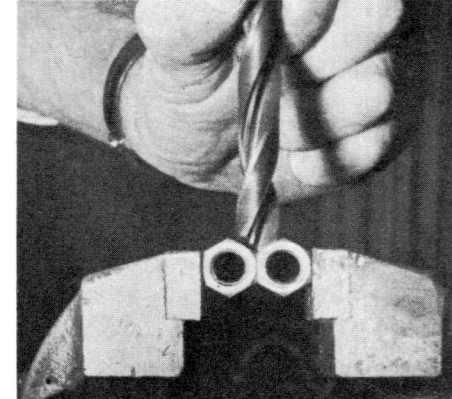

Checking the angles of the cutting edges.

Before offering the drill up to the grinder adjust the workrest to about the same level as the centre of the wheel. Then place the drill on the rest so that it lies horizontal (see Fig 3) and with the cutting lip level. It should also be at an angle of 59 to 60 deg with the face of the wheel (see Fig 4). A guide line cut into the rest may help.

The cutting edge should then be pushed against the wheel and slowly raised by pushing down on the shank using slow deliberate strokes. The drill must be frequently cooled in water to prevent overheating and 'drawing' the temper.

Fig. 3

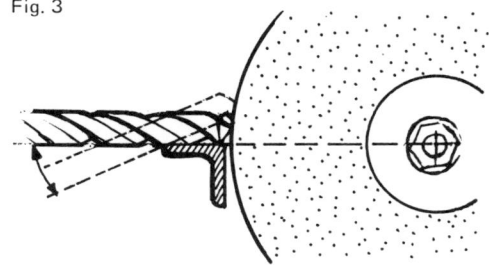

Correct position for grinding clearance angles.

Fig. 4

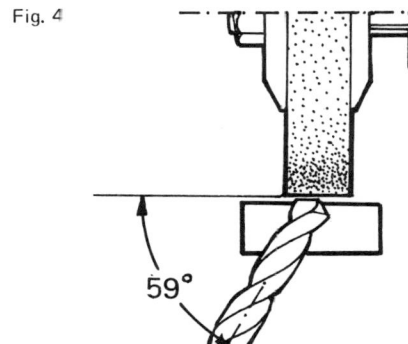

59°

Correct position for grinding cutting angles.

## DRILL STAND

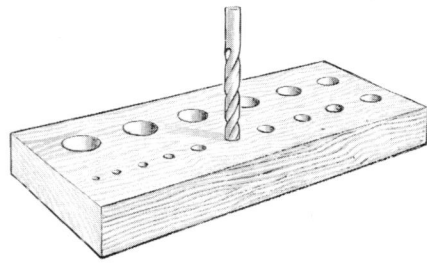

Often small drills are bought and used only a few times before they are mislaid or lost because there is no proper place to keep them. Store your drills tidily and undamaged in this cheap, simple-to-make drill stand. An off-cut of a 10 cm x 2 cm plank and half an hour's work is all that is needed.

Mark a guide line 2.5 cm from both edges of the plank and drill a hole for each size of drill, working down from the biggest to the smallest. Cut to length, clean up any splinters and each drill will stand in its own hole for easy selection.

## SPARES AND DRILLS

Keeping machines fully occupied when conditions are right depends as much on the spare part situation as on the vagaries of the weather.

An adequate stock of the most used cheaper spares, and knowing where to get the more expensive ones in a hurry, is vital. Familiarity with parts, and knowing how to identify them so that a trip to the dealer is not wasted, is equally important.

Even seemingly simple items like nuts and bolts need correct identification of at least six points. Using a poor substitute for the right nut and bolt and packing with washers often increases wear.

Look at the shape of the top of bolt head, the shape underneath the head and the shape of the nut. Then decide the metal used, the type of thread and, lastly, the size—length and diameter.

Before dismantling, find out what made the particular part fail. It is no use replacing one piece only to find it fractures again because of malfunction of its neighbour. If necessary list all the parts concerned.

Power drills require firm support with ample working room for boring awkward structures. Eric Clayton, an agricultural contractor, of Carlton, Sedgefield, Durham, has mounted this 2.5 cm heavy duty power drill on a tapered section. This is in turn spot welded to a steel section roof support stanchion.

Various ways of stocking spares and keeping a check so that they never run out have already been discussed in this series. Failure to order in advance can upset the best-laid plans and one way to avoid this is illustrated here.

Keep a list of the problems and the bits and pieces required in the tool-box of each of the more complex machines. A periodic check when someone is going to the dealer can save journeys and make sure the parts are to hand on the wet day, when the job will get done.

## OILING THE DRILL

A short piece of rubber hose fitted over the end of a drill prevents oil from being thrown away from the cutting edges during the vital stages of drilling. It also saves having to stop drilling each time a squirt of oil is necessary.

The reservoir between the hose and the drill ensures a constant supply of oil to the drill tip, thus keeping it cool.

Clearance between the hose and drill should be sufficient to prevent it being fouled by metal cuttings.

The rubber ring—well clear of the drill—forms the oil reservoir.

## CHOOSING AND USING A GRINDSTONE

Maintenance on most farms involves sharpening forage or beet harvester blades and small tools, and a power grindstone will do the job quickly and efficiently.

The two main types are either bench-mounted or pedestal. For a farm workshop where only minor repairs and maintenance are carried out a bench-mounted grindstone will be adequate and cheaper.

Where major repairs and a lot of welding and fabrication is carried out the pedestal type is best as the extra power is useful for removing metal in welding preparation.

Look for a machine that is well guarded and has an adjustable fence stop to prevent fingers and metal being dragged into the wheel. Some machines have a water reservoir fitted for cooling the object being ground. This is useful for cooling small tools but a bucket of water beside the machine is needed for cooling big jobs.

Spare grinding wheels are useful and will extend the range of the grindstone. If you can afford it buy several wheels of different coarseness to suit the different jobs you expect to do.

Make sure when fitting a different wheel on the spindle that the retaining nut is tight and the wheel spins true before switching on.

Provided you work carefully and use the full width of the wheel it will remain in good condition for a long time. Eventually it will wear and need trueing up again. Dressing the wheel can be done several ways. A piece of agate stone is a cheap dressing tool. Hold the agate firmly against the wheel until the high spots start wearing down. Move it gently across the width of the wheel until even grinding is restored.

Another method is to use a dresser. A cheap one consists of several serrated steel washers and spacers that revolve when moved across the wheel and wear down high spots. More expensive is a small steel rod with a conical end tipped with an industrial diamond. Whichever dresser you use always make sure the wheel is wet.

Always wear goggles and make sure guards are in position before switching on.

Do not press metal into the stone too hard and stall the machine. Apart from damaging the motor and bearings, chips may fly off the stone. If a crack appears on a wheel or a piece flies off stop the machine immediately and replace the wheel. An old damaged wheel invites trouble, as it will be out of balance and may disintegrate. Apart from the danger to the user an out of balance wheel will soon ruin spindle bearings.

Always use the whole face of the wheel to even out wear and prolong the life of the wheel. Little and often is the watchword with small tools such as twist drills and chisels. Cool them frequently to prevent overheating and turning blue or they will lose their hardness.

Set the fence close to the wheel to protect fingers.

Compare the badly worn wheel on the right with the new grindstone on the left.

A wheel chipped like this must be replaced immediately. It is out of balance and may disintegrate when it is used.

## GRINDERS

Blunt tools waste time and can be dangerous. Every farm workshop should have some kind of grinder for sharpening tools and it will also come in useful for the numerous odd jobs, such as shaping metal and parts which are too hard to file.

Grinders may be bought in various sizes and with a wide range of wheels.

A hand-operated unit which clamps to the bench is handy for small work and has the advantage of being portable. But it is limited in its use by the fact that one hand is taken up turning the handle. This makes it difficult to grind large pieces of tackle.

Grinding wheels are still made in imperial measures although some catalogues may quote metric equivalent sizes resulting from arithmetic conversion of units.

A 7in power unit combining a wire brush and fine-to-medium wheel will sharpen anything from an $\frac{1}{8}$ in drill to a forage harvester rotor blade, and has the added advantage of the wire brush for cleaning and preparing metal for welding.

When selecting a grinder it is important to get a strong, well-built one with sturdy adjustable work rests. Deciding on the grade of wheel depends on the type of work. All wheels have a grade number which represents the size of particles used to make it. For example, a grain of 36 means that the particles will pass through a screen with 36 meshes to the inch.

For high-speed work where a polished surface is not required, a 30 grain wheel is ideal, but for sharpening drills or chisels a medium fine 80 grain is best. It is a simple job to change wheels, and having two or three different grades is a good idea. This will overcome the problem of ruining a fine tool-sharpening wheel by having to use it for the rougher work.

The speed at which a wheel is driven is important, the faster it turns the smoother it will grind. Hand grinders should be turned at a fast, steady speed but not to the point where the gears start to whine or the wheel vibrates. With power-driven wheels there is always the danger of overheating the work and drawing the temper. Care must be taken to keep the cutting edges of tools such as drills and chisels cool. Moving the tool from side to side while grinding and allowing rests every few seconds will reduce this danger but frequent dipping in water may produce stress cracks particularly in high grade tool steels.

Wheels often become glazed and the pores get clogged with dirt and the softer metals, such as brass or aluminium, and become grooved and misshapen. There is no need to scrap a wheel when it gets into this state, it can be given a new lease of life if dressed. An inexpensive dressing tool can be bought and by simply holding it firmly against the wheel while it is turning, a new true cutting surface is restored.

It is advisable to wear goggles while grinding even when a glass shield is fitted and, as a further precaution, to reduce the danger from bits of

Large industrial grinders are best for rough work. They may be picked up cheaply from engineering companies who are in the process of retooling.

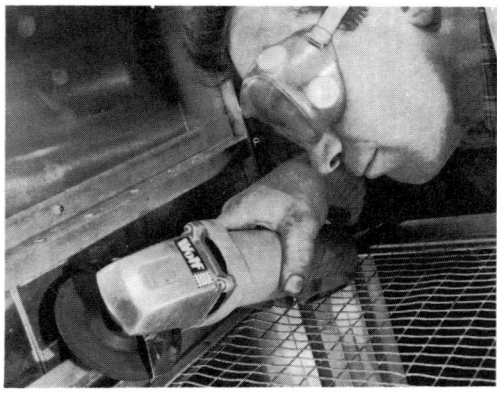
At the other end of the scale. This mini hand unit is ideal for getting into awkward corners.

flying metal and sparks, stand to one side of the wheel. The work rest must be set as close to the wheel as possible without actually touching it. If it is too far from the wheel, the work being ground could catch or wedge between the wheel and the rest and possibly chip or break the wheel or bend the spindle.

PORTABLE BENCH GRINDER
Grinders take up valuable bench space and often get in the way.

Mr. John Fountain, machinery lecturer at Aylesbury College of Further Education, came up with this idea (figs 1 and 2) to overcome the problem.

Instead of bolting the grinder to the bench top he mounted it on a base plate of 3 mm mild steel with a length of 50 x 50 x 6 mm angle-iron welded along the front edge.

The angle-iron holds the grinder in position and prevents it from being pushed on to the bench. The whole unit can be removed from the bench (fig 2) and taken to another part of the farm.

FILES
Many jobs in the farm workshop can be done faster and better with a file than with a grinding wheel. But to get the best work from your files a few rules must be adhered to.

Always use a new file on soft metal, such as brass or aluminium, then on slightly harder metal like cast iron before introducing it to steel. This allows the teeth to 'temper' and makes them less

Fig. 1 The grinder can be used normally. . .

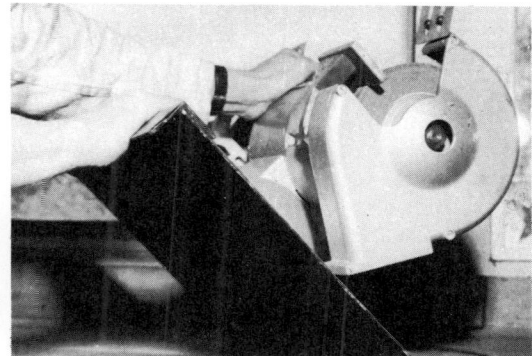
Fig. 2 . . .but is easily moved about

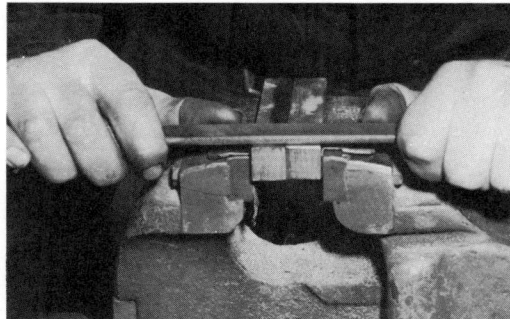
Draw filing to overcome clogging—an excellent way to file narrow surfaces. Pressure is applied to and fro.

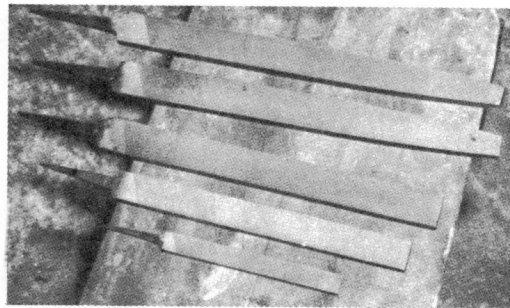
(Top to bottom) 14in flat bastard (30 teeth per inch) mainly for rough work; 12in second cut (40) with teeth running diagonally for smoother work: 12in bastard with teeth running diagonally in two directions; 10in second cut for finer control; 6in smoothing file (50) ideal for sharpening mower knife sections.

prone to chipping or breaking if used directly on hard metals.

Do not throw them in a heap with spanners

and other tools. Keep them in a rack or file wallet. A file is made from hardened tool steel and the sharp cutting edges on its surface tend to be brittle.

The teeth often become clogged with small metal particles, especially when filing soft metal, and must be cleaned regularly with a wire brush so that the particles do not build up to the point where the teeth break off.

When filing use slow full-length strokes and do not allow the file to skid over the metal. Short fast jerky stokes do not give the teeth time to cut and the work is likely to vibrate and cause screeching. If used in this manner a file will cut unevenly and soon become dull.

Files are classified according to teeth, size, shape, use and coarseness of cut—rough, coarse, bastard, second cut, smooth and dead smooth. These terms vary with the size of file. For example, a 20 cm bastard file is finer than a 25 cm. A file with one series of teeth is known as a single cut and with two rows, which cross at an angle, a double cut.

Once a file has been used on steel it will be less efficient on soft metals and it is good practice to keep one side for soft and the other for hard metals.

It is as important to look after files properly as it is to know how to use them correctly.

A clogged file will not cut properly; it will probably scratch the surface instead. A wire brush should be used to clean files and rubbing

on chalk is said to minimise clogging (see next page).

To store files a simple wallet can be made by folding like a concertina, thick paper, cardboard or similar material, placing a file in each fold, bunching them together and tying with string.

Screw slotted angle-iron to a wall so that the slots form a rack for different sizes of file.

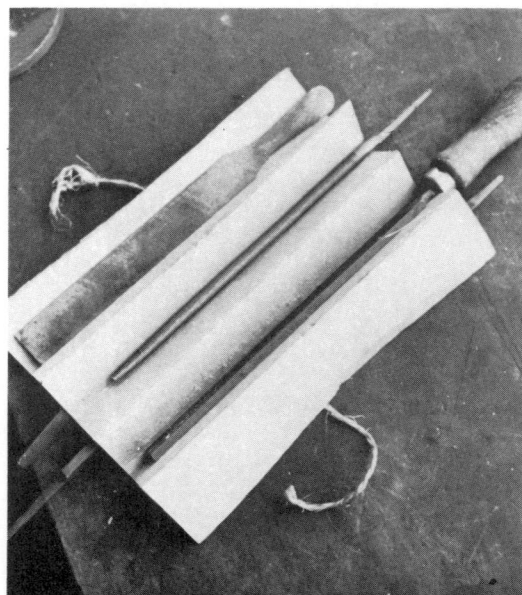

Make a simple wallet for them.

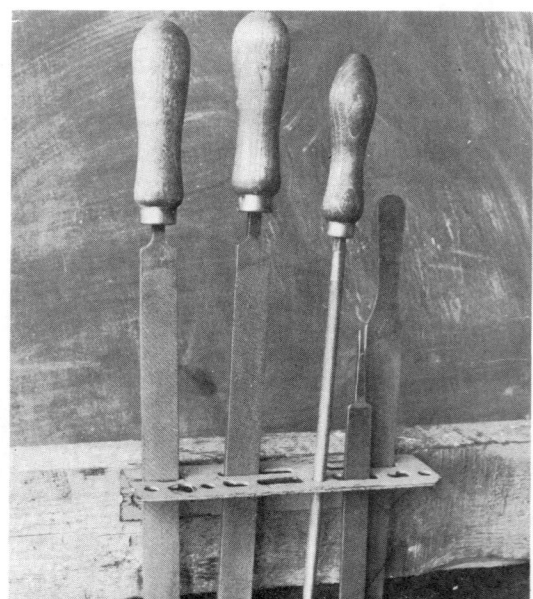

A piece of 'Dexion' type angle iron makes a good rack.

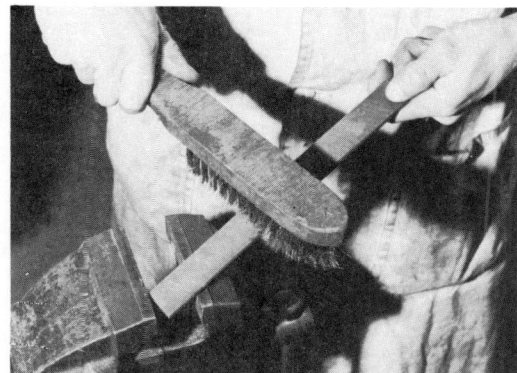

Cloggec files should be cleaned with a wire brush.

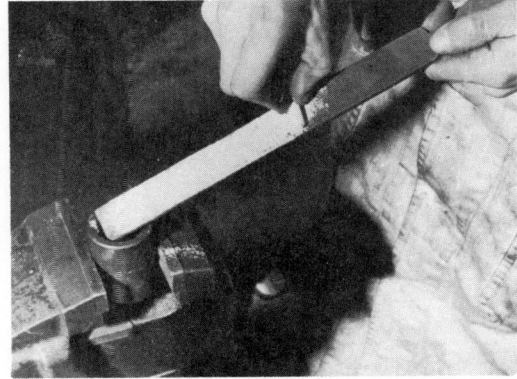

Rubbing chalk into the file keeps clogging to a minimum.

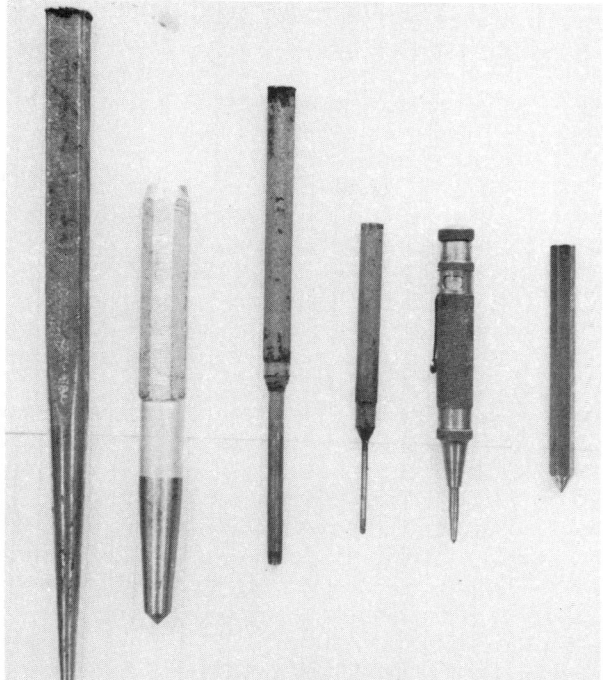

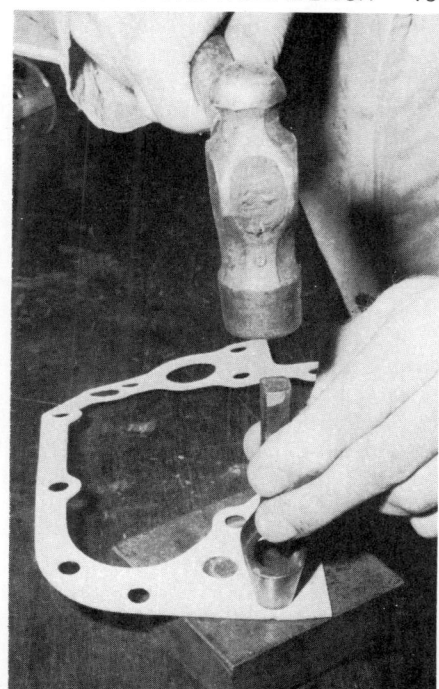

A selection of punches. From left: taper, centre, parallel or pin punches (two), spring-loaded centre punch made out of a broken **Allen key. Picture on the right shows a hollow punch in use.**

## CHOOSING A SET OF PUNCHES

The farm workshop should be equipped with three or four kinds of punch for removing pins, marking out jobs and for alignment purposes.

Parallel or pin punches are used to remove locating pins and rusted bolts. Choose the correct diameter parallel punch when knocking out split-pins; too small a punch may become stuck between the two halves of the pin.

Centre or dot punches are used for marking the centre of holes for drilling or for identifying the centre of a circle for compass points. Grind the point to an angle of about 60 deg.

Buy two centre punches, a small one for initial marking and a larger one to make a bigger mark once the first one has been checked. Always hold a centre punch vertically or it may slide when hit, leaving an inaccurate mark.

A spring-loaded centre punch works in the same way as a percussion hammer. Press the punch handle with the point on the metal and it will slide down the shaft, overcoming a spring pressure inside the handle to make a mark.

Taper punches are useful for lining up holes when fitting tinware. Push the punch through the hole next to the one in which you want to fit a bolt and it will pull the tin together, with the holes in line for the bolt. Screw this bolt in loosely and go on to the next. When all bolts are in they can be tightened.

Wad or hollow punches are circular hollow punches with a cutting edge ground on to the work end. Use them for cutting holes in homemade gaskets, canvas screens or other soft material. Never cut a hole in material lying on a steel surface; use a hardwood block between material and bench, to prevent damage to the cutting edge of the punch.

## TAKING CARE OF PUNCHES

Punches need little attention apart from keeping them correctly hardened and tempered and properly ground. There should be no mushrooming on the handle and the point should be kept clean and free from burrs.

Spreading on the hammer end of the punch is dangerous; bits may fly off when it is hit with a hammer and damage eyes or face. If the burrs are really bad through lack of attention over a long period place the punch head downwards on an anvil and with a hammer knock off the worst of the unwanted material. Clean off on a grindstone.

Grind the point a little at a time frequently dipping the punch in water to cool it and prevent loss of hardness.

If the punch gets too hot and needs rehardening use an acetylene torch to heat the metal to cherry-red heat along about a third of its length. Plunge it into water until cold. Clean the blade with emery cloth to see the colours formed by the re-tempering process.

Slowly reheat the punch. As the temperature increases the colours will begin to move slowly along the metal towards the point. When the edge is straw brown colour, plunge the point in water again.

Finally, lightly grind the punch and test for hardness with one or two light blows before hitting it hard.

This process can be used to harden all cutting tools.

## CARING FOR YOUR HACKSAW

Many workshop jobs of repairing or manufacturing call for the cutting of metals with a hacksaw. It is tempting to use whatever blade happens to be in the frame, but this is asking for broken blades.

A wide range of blades is sold, with teeth pitch ranging from 32 teeth per inch (tpi) for sheet metal to 14 tpi for cast iron. No metric sizes are available yet.

Blades are designed to cut on the forward stroke, but it is possible to obtain those which cut in both directions. Blades are usually $\frac{1}{2}$in wide and about 1/40 in thick.

Some are hardened and tempered to the same degree throughout, but the best type for the farm workshop has hardened teeth with the rest of the blade softer. Another type, which is about 1in wide, has teeth on both edges which are hardened while the centre of the blade is soft.

Both the soft-backed blade and soft-centred blade are ideal for cutting in awkward corners. They are less likely to break.

Make sure that the teeth are in line with the frame. Blades tend to twist when tightening the frame thumbscrew, making it difficult to cut straight.

Hacksaw blades are like files in that they will last longer if used initially for cutting soft metals such as brass, copper or aluminium. Cutting against a sharp corner is the quickest way to blunt a new blade. The initial strokes should be made away from the edge.

Another common fault is cutting too fast. This causes the teeth to get hot and lose their hardness: they do not have time to bite into the metal and will slide over the surface.

A blade with 18 tpi is best for all-round use. There should be at least two teeth completely in work at any one part of the stroke. Teeth should never straddle the work.

If thin sheet metal has to be cut by hacksaw and the only blade available is a coarse one, clamp several sheets together or clamp the sheet between wood.

Should a blade break half-way through a cut it is better to start again on the other side rather than force the new blade down the old groove.

## BROKEN HACKSAW BLADES
Awkward jobs for hacksaws can mean more breakages than usual—and blades are not cheap. Mr. H. V. Hinton, Hill Cottage, Lois Weedon, Towcester, Northants, thought up this idea for

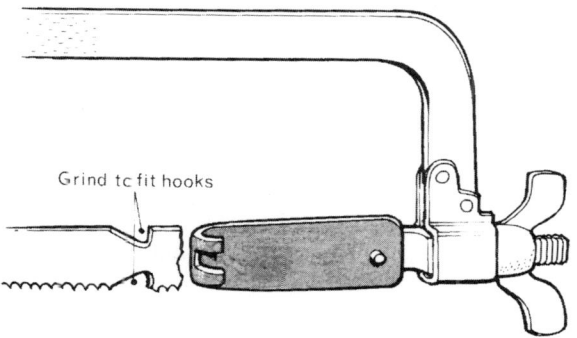

Grind to fit hooks

using blades which are still good except for their lost inches. A piece of mild steel file cut to match the length of broken blade and shaped with the twin hooks one end is drilled to fit the hacksaw frame at the other. Hook on and tighten as usual.

## FEELER GAUGES
Feeler gauges are used to measure critical clearances such as tappet, contact breaker or plug gaps, or to determine the number of shims required for bearings or cutter bars. You will probably need both an imperial and a metric set.

The gauges are made of hardened steel and there are generally 10 in a set, ranging from $1\frac{1}{2}$ to 25 thousandths of an inch thickness; in imperial measure or in metric units feelers are made in hundredths of mm and range from 5 hundredths of 1 mm to 100. A set of sizes 5 to 60 would cover most likely applications.

They are precision instruments and should be treated as such. When using them to measure a tappet clearance, for example, do not tighten the tappet hard down on the gauge. Adjust for a light dragging fit between the tappet and valve. A tight fit will scratch or dent the surface of the gauge, so making it inaccurate.

After use, clean the gauges, and store them in rust-inhibiting paper, or smear them with light oil, wrap in an oily rag and store in a dry place.

Rusty gauges can be startlingly inaccurate, especially when two or more are used together.

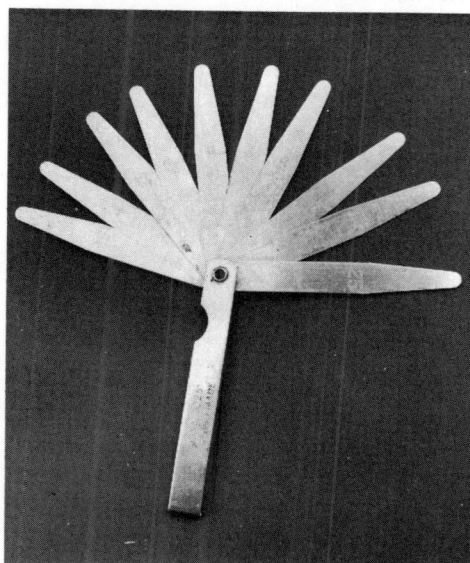

## COLD CHISELS
Cold chisels are made from high carbon or nickel alloy tool steel and are tempered for cutting cold metals. They must be kept sharp—and sharpening entails more than giving the edge a quick rub on the emery wheel. Hold the chisel in the right hand and keep it firmly against the grinder work rest with the index finger touching the underside of the rest. Press the cutting edge against the wheel with the first two fingers of the left hand and

move it back and forth across the wheel with a wrist action. This produces a slightly curved edge by grinding more off the two corners, which helps prevent their breaking off and reduces the danger of drawing the temper through over-heating.

To ensure that the cutting angle is correct, a simple gauge can be made from a small piece of sheet metal (see diagram).

The harder the metal to be cut, the greater the cutting angle and vice-versa. A 40 deg angle is best for soft metals, 60—70 deg for mild steel, and for hard metal, 75—80 degrees.

To ensure replacing it in the original grinding

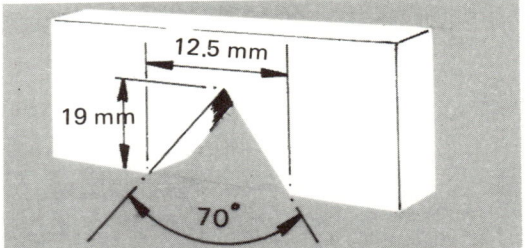

Jagged burrs should be removed long before they reach this stage. A couple of minutes on the grinder could save injuring the hand.

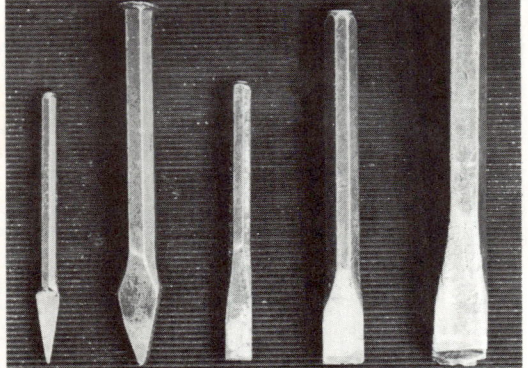

(From left to right) Nos. 1 and 2: Cross-cut chisels for cutting rectangular grooves such as keyways. Nos. 3, 4 and 5: Flat chisels for chipping flat or convex surfaces and cutting in general. The damaged cutting edge of No. 5 is the result of continual overheating during sharpening.

position after inspecting and cooling, make sure that you do not move the hand gripping the chisel shank. The index finger will then contact the work rest in exactly the same position.

Chisels should be the right size for the job.

Using a light one for heavy work may shatter it and it will certainly vibrate and sting the hand.

When cutting or dressing metal on an anvil always use the soft surface working face. Cutting right through a piece of metal on to the hardened surface will not only blunt the chisel, but damage the face of the anvil. The same goes for work held in a vice: keep the chisel away from the hardened jaws.

## USING A MICROMETER

When measuring critical dimensions such as the diameter of a shaft or the width of a key, a micrometer gives extreme accuracy.

An external micrometer consists of a frame with a spindle and a barrel at one end and the anvil or fixed jaw at the other. The barrel has an internal thread and calibrations on the outside. The spindle is screwed into the thread and moved by turning the thimble on the barrel.

Place the jaws of the micrometer over the object to be measured and, by turning the thimble, move the spindle until the jaws lightly grip the object. Read the measurement off the barrel.

It is important that the jaws are not tightened too much, otherwise they will become strained and the extra pressure put on the fine thread inside the barrel may damage it.

To ensure that the jaws are not over-tightened some micrometers have a ratchet attached to the thimble and this slips when a pre-set pressure is

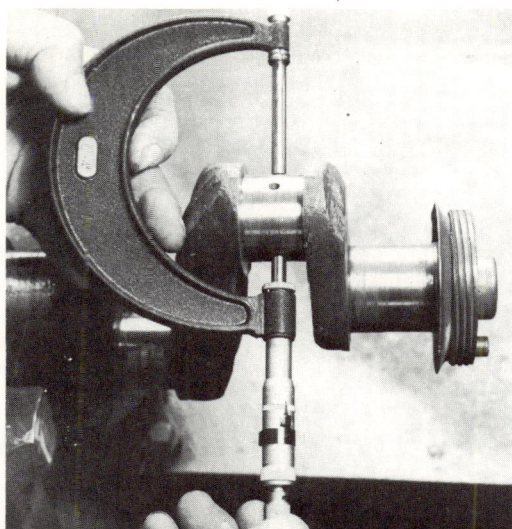

Measuring the diameter of a crankshaft. Remember to use the ratchet to screw up the jaws.

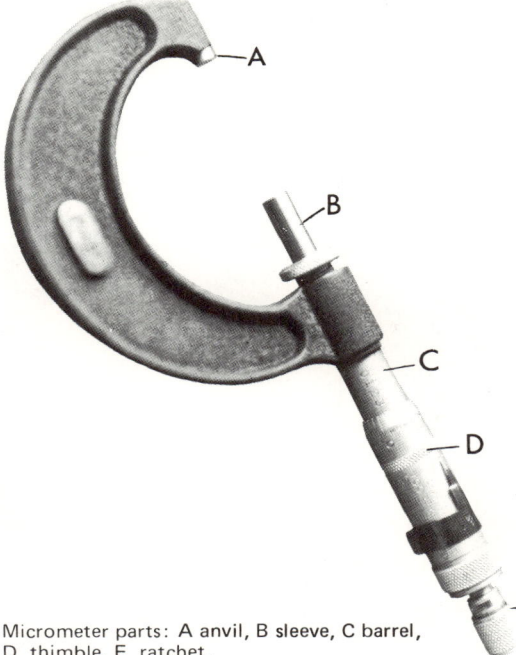

Micrometer parts: A anvil, B sleeve, C barrel, D thimble, E ratchet.

reached. Remember that using the ratchet to screw up the jaws gives great accuracy.

For the farm workshop two micrometers should suffice—an ordinary 0—25 mm fixed anvil micrometer for small dimensions and an adjustable 0—100 mm for most of the bearings and shafts likely to be encountered on the farm.

If your workshop is big enough to justify one, buy an internal micrometer as well. But a skilled mechanic will be able to use a pair of internal calipers and an ordinary micrometer to measure internal diameter.

## THE METRIC MICROMETER

The screw has a pitch of ½ mm; therefore two revolutions of the thimble will move the spindle a distance of 1 mm.

### Sleeve

The datum line is graduated with two sets of lines, the group above reading in millimetres, the group below in half-millimetres.

### Thimble

The scale is marked in fifty equal divisions, in groups of five, each small division representing 1/50 of ½ mm which equals 1/100 mm (0.01 mm).

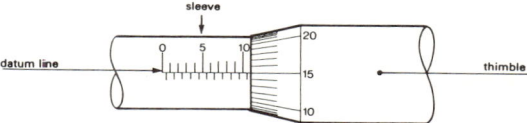

### To Read the Micrometer

1. Read the number of whole millimetre divisions on the sleeve (major divisions).
2. Observe whether or not there is a half-millimetre division visible (minor divisions).
3. Read the thimble for hundredths (thimble divisions), i.e. the line on the thimble coinciding with the datum line.

| | | |
|---|---|---|
| Major divisions | 10 x 1.00 mm = | 10.00 mm |
| Minor divisions | 1 x 0.50 mm = | 0.50 mm |
| Thimble divisions | 15 x 0.01 mm = | 0.15 mm |
| | Reading = | 10.65 mm |

## THE IMPERIAL MICROMETER

The screw has 40 threads per inch so one complete revolution moves 1/40in (0.025in) and in 1/25 of a turn it will move 1/25 of 1/40in (0.001in).

## Sleeve

This has the major divisions marked on it representing tenths of an inch, i.e. 0.100in. Each major division is sub-divided into four minor divisions representing 0.025in each.

## Thimble

This is divided into twenty-five parts and as one full turn is equal to one minor division on the sleeve (0.025in) each division on the thimble will be 0.001in.

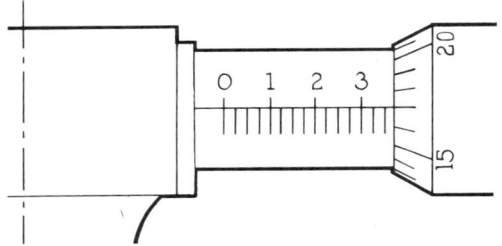

## To Read the Micrometer

1. Read the number of tenths (major divisions).
2. Add the number of minor divisions multiplied by 0.025in.
3. Add the number of thousandths on the thimble, i.e. the line on the thimble coinciding with the datum line.

| | |
|---|---|
| Major divisions | 3 × 0.100in = 0.300in |
| Minor divisions | 2 × 0.025in = 0.050in |
| Thimble divisions | 17 × 0.001in = 0.017in |
| | Reading = 0.367in |

## VARIABLE MICROMETERS

There are two types of external micrometers. One has a fixed anvil and the other has a removable anvil. With the removable type one can get a set of anvils in varying lengths (0—10 cm or 0—15 cm) and by changing the jaw can measure a wide range of sizes with one micrometer.

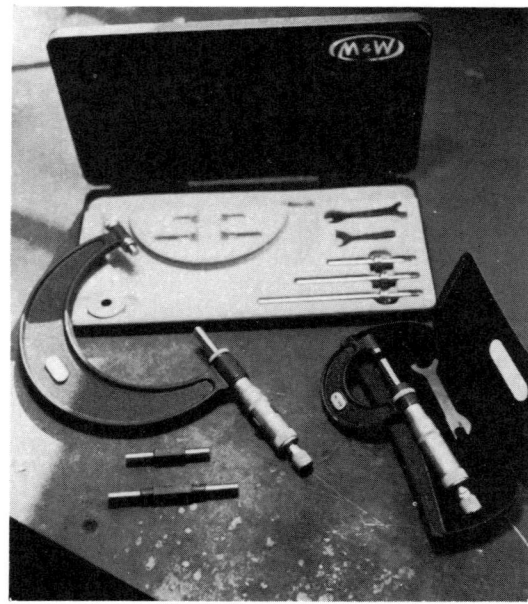

Right: a fixed anvil micrometer. The larger, variable type is on the left. Interchangeable anvils are in the box, with the master gauges at bottom left.

To change the jaws a set of spanners is provided with the micrometer. Take out one jaw and substitute another, making sure it has seated correctly. Before use check the micrometer for accuracy with a master gauge or a piece of known size, in case the new jaw has not seated or dirt has stopped it screwing in fully.

Check with a master piece of 5 cm diameter; if the micrometer reads zero when the master piece is measured then all is correct. If it reads 0.2 mm over size, on all readings you will subtract 0.2 mm to give an accurate measurement and vice versa if the reading, when checked on the master piece, is low.

Never swap parts of one micrometer with parts of another; each micrometer is made and calibrated separately so that it is only accurate with its own parts.

Cleanliness is essential for good results. Before a measurement is taken, clean off all dirt and grease from the part to be measured or a false reading may be obtained.

Do not ill-treat the micrometer by giving it a hard knock, or its accuracy will soon be lost. When it has been used, clean it with a dry rag and store it in a dry place with a layer of rust-preventing paper.

## TAPS AND DIES

When a machine is overhauled a thread in a casting or an adjusting rod is often damaged. If the thread is not excessively damaged it is possible and cheaper to renovate it by using taps or dies than to buy a new part.

A tap is a bolt made of high carbon steel with a perfect thread, and cutting edges have been provided by placing flutes along the tap. One end of the tap is squared so that it can be screwed into the hole to be threaded with an adjustable tap wrench. When the tap is screwed into the correct sized hole it will cut an internal thread that will fit a bolt of the same size.

There are two types of tap; one is a taper with its leading end tapered off for the first few threads so letting the tap enter the hole and cut a full thread gradually. The second is a plug tap that cuts for its whole length and is used as a finishing tap in a 'blind' hole that requires a full thread to the bottom of the hole.

A die is used for cutting external threads on round bar or tube and consists of a high carbon steel nut with parts of its circumference cut away. The portion of nut left cuts into the bar and leaves a thread. A die is held in a 'stock' or handle and is held in position by a set screw. There are several forms of dies but the most common one is split, allowing a small adjustment to be made in the thread size by means of screws in the stock. Using this adjustment ensures a good fit in the thread to the nut used.

A set of taps and dies of sizes from $\frac{1}{4}$ to $\frac{3}{4}$ inch in one-sixteenth steps with two taps and a die for each size will cover most farm uses. Similarly, a metric set covering a similar range, say

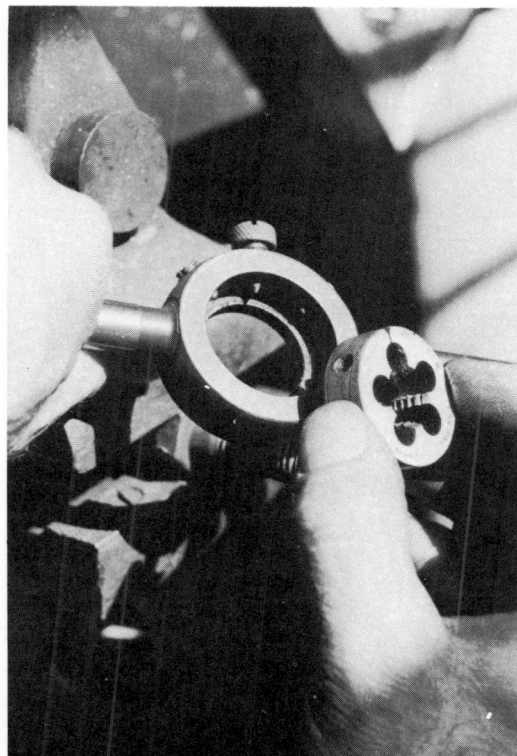

The die fits into the stock with the tapered threads of the die farthest from the shoulder in the stock.

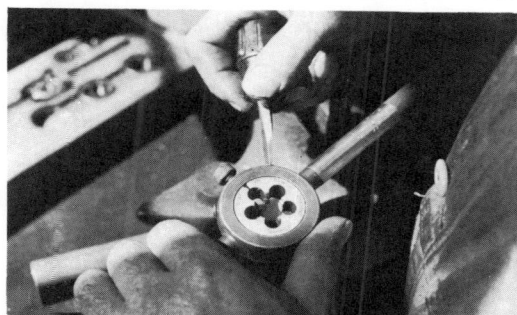

The adjusting screws to hold the die tight in the stock and to allow small alterations to be made in the size of the thread.

A taper tap on the right and a plug tap on the left showing the first few threads on the taper tap gradually leading to a full thread.

from 5 mm to 20 mm in 1 or 2 mm steps will be increasingly desirable. Other than metric threads, the most useful tap and die sets are likely to be Unified Coarse and Unified Fine but there are still quite a few B.S. Whitworth bolts about.

Buy a tin of cutting compound for use with your taps and dies. It will lubricate the cutting edges and help to get a good finish. Compound is unnecessary when threading a cast iron casting —there is enough graphite in the iron to provide lubrication.

## CUTTING A THREAD:
## TAPPING AND DIEING

When a threaded hole is needed in metal a hole must first be drilled to allow the tap to cut a full thread. For a three-eighths diameter bolt thread the right size drill is five-sixteenths. Similarly for a metric thread use a drill one size smaller than the tap to be used.

Too small a drill hole will mean the tap will have to cut extra material, it will be difficult to turn and may break off in the hole.

Too large a hole will not allow the full thread to be cut and a loose fit will result in a weak thread. Often the drill size is stamped on the tap. Most tool manufacturers print a chart of corresponding hole and tap sizes. Hang one in the workshop where it can be easily seen.

Having drilled the hole select the appropriate size taper tap and lightly smear it with a little cutting compound. This will improve the cutting

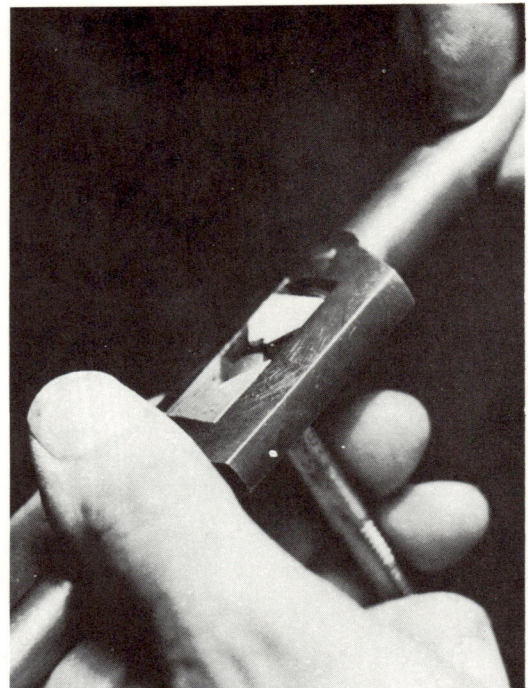

Fix the tap securely in the tap wrench. If it is not held squarely, it will twist round with the action of tapping, and damage the soft jaws of the wrench.

After the tap has begun to bite into the metal, check that it is entering the hole squarely. A lopsided thread is very difficult to correct after the first few turns.

action and help give a good finish to the threads. Use the compound sparingly: too much will allow the swarf to stick to the tap instead of falling away. It may get jammed

and cause a rough thread to be cut. Insert the tap into the hole and, making sure it is at right angles to the work, screw it into the metal until you feel it cutting. Check again that the tap is perpendic-

Grinding a bevel on a piece of bar. This will ensure that the die cuts into the bar gradually and corrections can be made if the die is not straight.

ular to the work by standing a small square on the work and moving it alongside the tap. Turn the tap into the work reversing it slightly every half turn or so to clear the swarf. When the hole has fully threaded run the plug tap through to finish off.

If a blind hole is being threaded, remove the tap occasionally and blow out the accumulated swarf. When the taper tap has reached the bottom of the hole finish off again with the plug tap taking care not to break it off.

If you break a tap off in the hole and it will not twist out, try to remove it by placing a small dot punch on the broken portion and knocking it round with a hammer. If this fails it will have to be drilled out and a larger size hole tapped.

For dieing a bar down use the same principle. Make sure, from manufacturers' charts, that the bar is the correct diameter for the die. Grind a small 45 deg bevel on the end of the bar to allow the die to cut gradually into the metal. Check that the die is squarely on the bar or a lopsided thread will be cut.

## QUICK ANVIL
You can make yourself a small anvil like the one pictured from a 30 cm length of railway line drilled and bolted to the bench.

## CHOOSING THE RIGHT HAMMER
Hammers are probably the most commonly used

tools in the workshop and also are the most abused. Often the wrong type is used for a job.

Hammers are classified according to shape of head and weight. Two or three different types will suffice for most jobs on the farm and in the workshop. Most common type in use in engineering is the ball pein, with one end of the head ball-shaped and the other end flat. Despite metrication, this is another example of a range of tools that are still made almost entirely in established imperial measure and sold the same way too.

Peining is the act of striking a small area of metal a number of light blows with the object of stretching the metal slightly.

From left: 2lb ball pein, 1lb cross pein, copper and rawhide soft hammer, mason's hammer, 1lb claw hammer, ½lb ball pein and a 14lb sledge hammer.

Other types of peining hammer are the cross pein and the straight pein, with a blunt-pointed head across the shaft of the handle and down the shaft respectively.

Other types of hammer include the claw, used for extracting nails, the bigger club or mason's hammer for heavy work and the sledge for a really big job.

The 'soft' hammer or mallet avoids damaging a finished surface and yet can have some force applied, for example, when knocking a bearing on to a shaft.

Soft hammers are two headed, with one head of copper or lead and the other of hide. Both heads are easily replaced. For the big job use a 7lb or 14lb sledge-hammer.

Hammer heads are usually made of medium carbon steel. The striking ends are hardened for long life and the middle portion, where the handle fits, is left soft. Never strike a blow with a middle portion which will easily lose its shape, causing the handle to work loose.

Hammer handles are made of metal or, more commonly, of wood, such as hickory or ash for toughness and strength combined with cheapness.

Make sure the handle is tight and free from cracks. When fitting a new one, always use two wedges—one wood, one metal—to hold the handle on the head. The wooden wedge should be driven in with the grain of the wood in the groove provided in the end of the handle. The metal wedge goes across the grain and helps hold the wooden one in position.

Use a 2lb or 3lb hammer for a big chiselling job such as hacking a rusted nut off a shaft. For a delicate job, such as tapping out a gasket, use a half-pounder.

Grip the hammer at the end of the shaft to exert the maximum force and use an easy rhythmic swing on to the surface to be struck. Take an aiming tap between each main blow until you are sure of your aim.

## THE RIGHT RIVET

Most components of modern farm machinery are fastened into position by bolts, spot welding or dowels, but there are still instances where the rivet is used to join parts.

Three main types of rivet are used. One is the countersunk rivet when a flush surface is needed. Because part of the main strength of a rivet is in

Three main types of rivet, from left: round head rivet, countersunk and pan head, which is the strongest type.

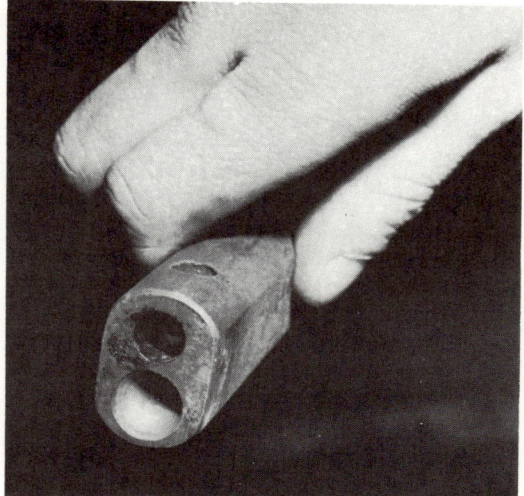

This snap is used first to tighten the joint, then to form the rivet head.

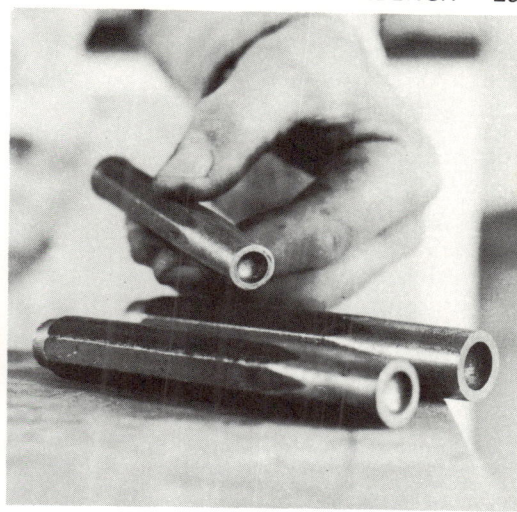

The rivet snap. Hemispherical recess in the end of the snap is hammered over the rivet to form a strong head.

the head which prevents components pulling apart, this type is not as strong as the other two—the pan head and the round head. The round head is rounded and the pan head is bulkier—the strongest of the three.

The strength of the finished job also depends on the tightness of the rivet in the joint. For this reason it is essential to use the correct size. If it is too small the rivet will not spread in the hole sufficiently and will allow movement. The strain on the rivets will be too great and they will

shear. The correct sized rived should pass comfortably through the hole and when expanded, grip the metal of the parts that are being joined.

If the rivet holes have worn oval they must be welded up and redrilled or a loose joint will result.

**Length** of rivet is also crucial. If it is too short the rivet will not protrude far enough through its hole to allow a strong head to be formed. Aim to have about 1½ times the diameter of the rivet showing above the surface.

To make a neat job of forming the head use a rivet snap. This is a high carbon steel 'punch' with a semi-circular recess in one end. This is placed over the rivet and the other end is hit with a hammer. The rivet head takes the form of the recess. There is a range of snap sizes to form the right head on any common sized rivet.

There are two basic methods of riveting: hot riveting that entails heating the rivet up to a cherry red heat before placing it in the parts to be joined, and cold riveting. Usually hot riveting is used only on larger rivets as it is easier to form the head of the rivet and to get a better finished job. As it cools the metal contracts, pulling the surfaces together to give a tight joint. Cold riveting is used generally on smaller jobs such as a mower section.

## SCREWDRIVER SALVAGE

The screwdriver with a broken handle can still be useful. Cut off the handle and weld a piece of $\frac{3}{8}$ in diameter bar across the top. Screws that resist an ordinary screwdriver and normal force should be beaten by this one. The handles will allow you to exert a greater downward force on the head of the screw and prevent the blade slipping from the slot. You will also get more leverage.

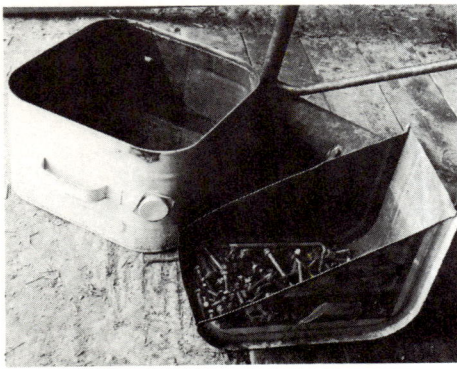

## STORAGE OF NUTS AND BOLTS

When nuts and bolts are a jumbled mass in one box it can take longer to find a certain size of bolt than it takes to fit it. Here are two alternatives. (Above) Lengths of timber nailed together form a cradle to hold bins made from otherwise scrap oil drums. The bins are handy for carrying a selection of bolts round the workshop or to the field. (Left) Drums with one end cut out make multi-purpose containers.

## CONTAINER CONVERSION

Cut one side out of a one gallon polythene container with a sharp knife to make a simple but effective storage container for nuts, bolts and small spare parts.

Mr. Thomas Fothergill, Rectory Farm, Thornton-le-Clay, Yorks., has gone one better and made a rack of containers by placing a fencing rail through the handles of the containers and siting them alternately left and right to enable him to see at a glance what each container holds.

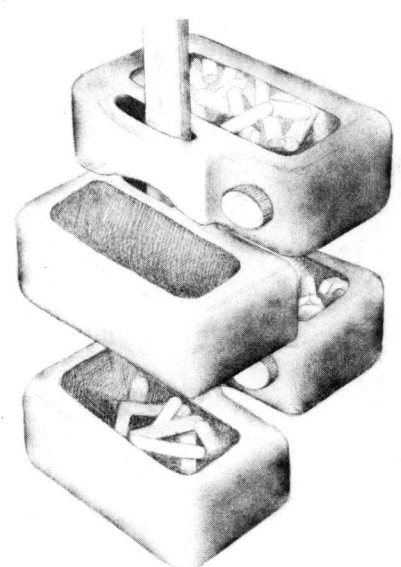

## NUTS AND WASHERS STORED

Nuts and washers are often stored in the same drawer or tin on the bench and when one is required it takes a long time sorting through them to find the size required.

Save yourself this trouble by stringing nuts and washers on a **length of 6 mm welding rod with a** label on the end stating size and thread. Hang the rods on nails in the tool store for easy access.

## SPARES

A well-equipped workshop must have a stock of spare parts, nuts, bolts, washers and other materials to back it up. Quick repair kits for each piece of tackle is probably the best and cheapest way. Contained in individual boxes they can be stored easily and, more important, found when needed.

Label each item with its part number and supplier and when it is used the label is removed and placed in a box with the name of the supplier stamped on the side.

The supplier's representative, when he calls, orders from the label which is then transferred to an 'on-order' box. The part is delivered and has the label tied on before going into the repair kit.

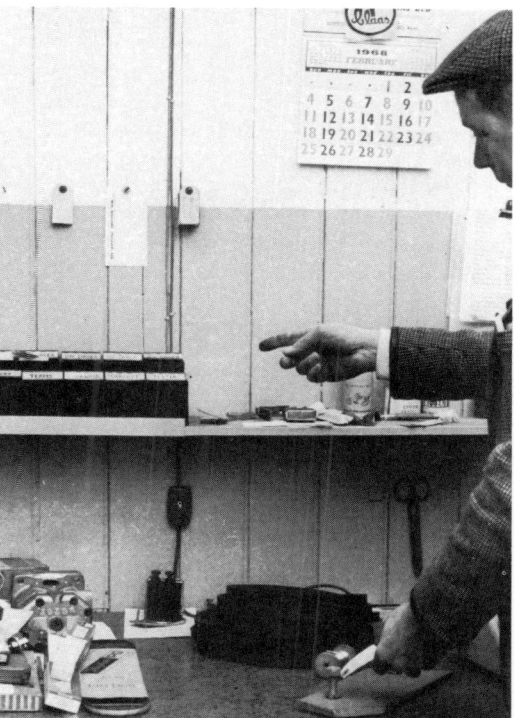

# EVERY MAN HIS OWN MECHANIC

### TOWING VEHICLE HITCH

It is always handy to be able to change the hitch of a towing vehicle from ball to clevis. Mr. Peter Glower, Garford, Abingdon, Berks, made up this kit for his Land-Rover. The grey ball hitch is on the vehicle and the clevis hitch also belongs to the vehicle but has been welded on to Mr. Glower's adaptation. The important point, he says, is to ensure that the pin is a snug fit behind the ball where the pull is taken.

Mr. J. Wild, Knowle Top Farm, Buxworth, Stockport, has another version. He uses a 20 cm piece of channel iron 100 mm x 75 mm by 6 mm thick and a 50 mm threaded ball bought from an agricultural engineer.

Drill two 25 mm holes in line through the channel and two through the back to enable it to be fastened to the back of the vehicle. Simply remove the ball to convert the hitch to a clevis.

### BALL HITCH

Another conversion of a ball hitch—this time to allow a low loader trailer normally towed by a Land-Rover on the road to be pulled behind a tractor and used for field work—comes from Mr. D. Smith, Willow Grange, Stanfield, Dereham, Norfolk.

Two pieces of 6 mm thick angle-iron are welded together to form a box section to fit between the drawbar jaws of an MF 165 tractor. The box section is drilled to allow the ball hitch to be bolted to it. Fit the box section between the drawbar jaws and make a mark either side of the top jaws. Weld two blocks of metal about 25 mm x 25 mm x 100 mm so that the edge of the blocks just touches the mark, yet allows the drawbar jaw to fit between them. These blocks will stop the attachment rotating about the drawbar when in use.

Finally, mark and drill a hole between the blocks through the box section to take the drawbar pin (see picture to right).

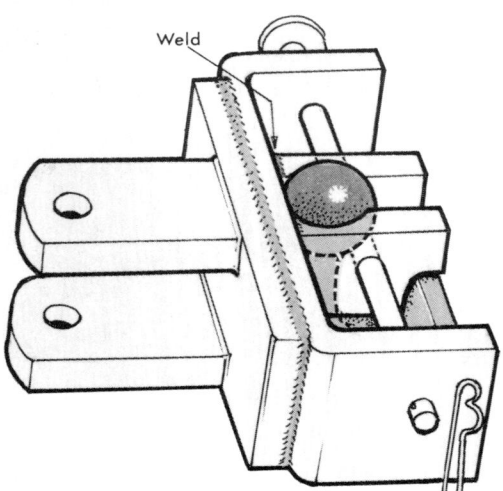

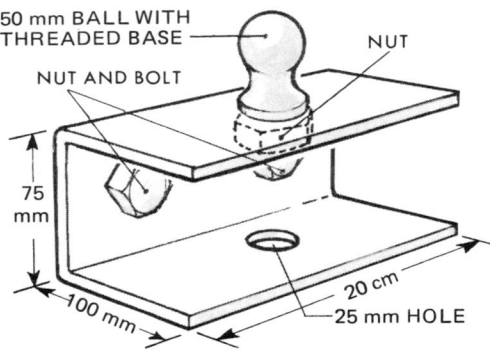

50 mm BALL WITH THREADED BASE

NUT

NUT AND BOLT

75 mm

100 mm

20 cm

25 mm HOLE

Weld

## SAFETY
Bear in mind that this sort of conversion may be useful for 'instant' hitch adaptation just for moving machines about in the yard. The hitches developed by Mr. Glower and Mr. Smith would not comply with regulations for use on public roads. The type developed by Mr. Wild would be expected to do so.

## HOME-MADE TRACTOR WEIGHT
Mr. Alan Barnsdale, The Hayward, Stubtop, Lincs, found that tractor wheel weights were inadequate and water ballasting was inconvenient. He made up a 350 kg three-point linkage-mounted weight out of: 180 litre oil barrel and some mild steel bar; 2 metres of 75 mm x 25 mm flat steel bar, 2 metres of 75 mm x 12 mm flat bar; a length of 12 mm diameter bar the length of the barrel.

First job is to cut one end out of the oil drum with an acetylene torch. Next saw the two lengths of flat bar in half and drill 12 mm diameter holes near the ends, and also in the centre of the closed end of the barrel. Run the 12 mm diameter bar through the centre of the barrel and make holes in the sides of the barrel to give good three-point linkage attachment points. Tack weld the strips of flat bar into position inside the drum and to the barrel sides. Fill the barrel with scrap iron or rubble and seal the end with a layer of cement and leave it to set.

To mount the weight on to the tractor fit category 2 linkage pins into the lower link mounting points and use a top link on the third attachment point. Use stabiliser bars to hold the weight rigid on the three-point linkage.

When the weight is not needed, it can be lowered on to the small saw-horse frame made out of 40 mm square tubing.

Main advantage of this type of weight is that the drawbar can be used with the weight in position.

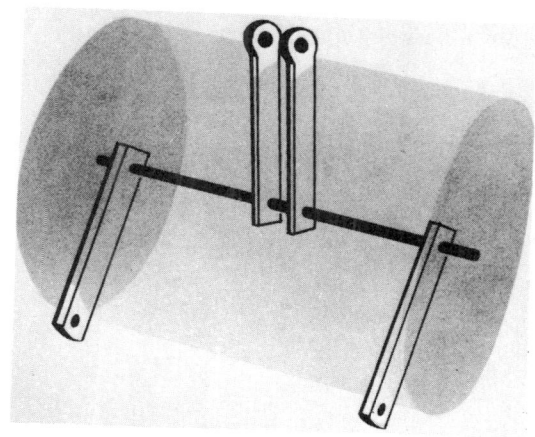

Because the weight is held on the tractor's hydraulics, avoid damage to ram seals by locking the three-point linkage in the raised position. This can be done mechanically on some tractors. Otherwise use a tee-piece similar to that used on the old Ferguson pick-up hitch in place of the normal top link.

## A TRANSPORT BOX

A transport box which can also be used for small-scale slurry carting has been developed by Mr. John Done, Mount Pleasant Farm, Hagworthingham, Spilsby, Lincs.

An ingenious top linkage arrangement is fitted to the box. Two plates hold a collar which can slide over a shaft. This shaft is connected to a swinging arm linking the stays, which cause the floor of the box to slide back and allow the slurry to run out while the box is in the raised position.

Mr. Done's transport box with floor open.

As the linkage is raised the distance between the plates at the top of the linkage and the swinging arm is reduced. If the connecting shaft is locked inside the collar it cannot slide, so it pushes the floor stays and opens the floor at the front.

For normal transport work, however, the lock is released, allowing the collar to slide up the connecting shaft as the box is raised, and the floor remains shut.

The locking is done by winding a handle at the end of the shaft which pushes out two tongues. There are three locking positions.

When the linkage is lowered the box floor is automatically pulled shut.

To tip the box backwards the top link is used in a position 50 cm from the lower links. To keep the box level a bolt is fastened to the floor through the connecting arms.

The back door lifts out and tipping the box in the normal way is simply a matter of turning a handle just above the top link, which releases a catch. This catch fastens again when the hydraulics are lowered.

## HARROW WING WINCH

To facilitate lifting the side wings on this 6.4 m wide Parmiter harrow at Berkshire College of Agriculture farm, the engineering department has fitted a hand-operated winch with cables to each wing section. The second-hand winch has been fitted centrally on the harrow headstock. Chains on the end harrows prevent them swinging outwards in transport.

This idea has cut out the need to remove the harrow sections and put them on the central harrow frame for transport, and made easier the job of moving the equipment from field to field.

The work involved bolting the winch to the harrow frame headstock, setting the cables to the right length and welding small shackles to each end and the inner harrow section to take the holding chains.

## SILAGE HARVESTER DRIVE PULLEY

Damage suffered by a silage harvester drive pulley which has probably been 'eased off' with a heavy stone, spanner or ordinary steel hammer.

Cost of replacement and loss of working time could have been avoided if a soft-faced hammer had been used.

## SAFE GRIP

When shortening a bolt in a vice avoid damage to the thread by threading two nuts on the bolt and tightening one against the other. Clamp the vice against these and saw off the unwanted portion.

As the nuts are taken off they will smooth out any roughness caused by the hacksaw at the end of the thread.

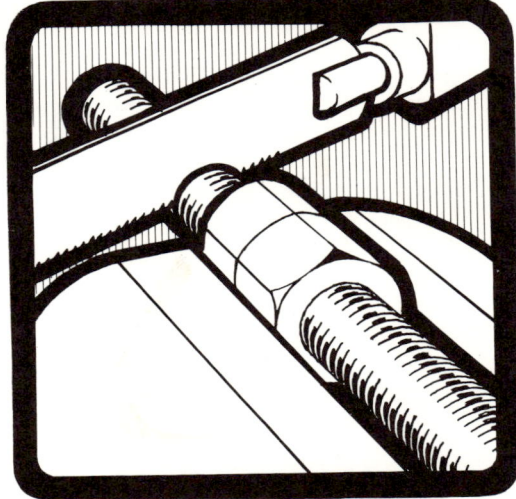

# NEW IDEAS

## DRILL CHUCK

Chuck keys for pillar drills are easily lost. Prevent this happening by attaching one end of a length of small-linked chain to the body of the drill and the other end to the key.

Tap a small hole in the drill casting, put a bolt through the end link and screw the bolt into the hole. Be careful to place the hole in the casting where the bolt will not interfere with the internal mechanics of the drill or weaken the casting excessively.

## PORTABLE TOOL EXTENSION CABLE

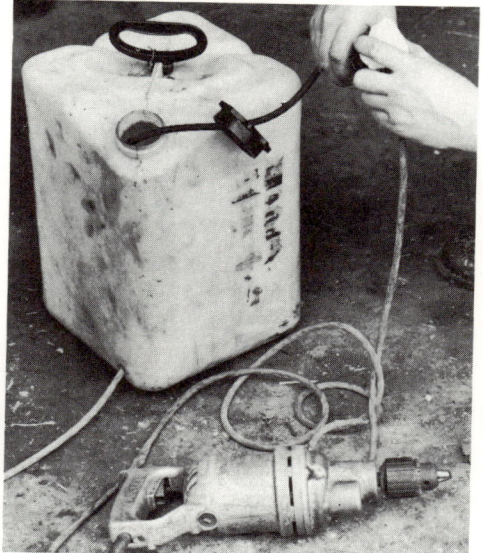

Users of portable electric tools will welcome this idea for storing extension cables. The cable is ready for instant use and can be carried easily. It is also protected against damage and the danger of shorting.

Bore a hole in the bottom corner of the container slightly smaller than the diameter of the cable. This prevents the cable from being pulled out from the wrong end. Next bore a hole in the

screw cap which is a snug fit and the insulating rubber. It may then be drawn along to remove dirt before the cable is fed into the container.

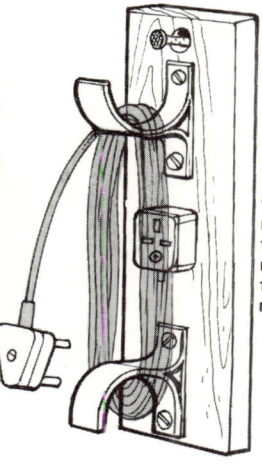

Neater ways of storing extension cables are always welcome.
Mr. T. Gill, Wigton, Cumberland, took a piece of board 1m long, 250 mm wide and 25 mm thick, mounted a 125 mm gutter bracket top and bottom and three-pin socket in the middle. Up to 50 metres can be carried and a hole at the top allows it to hang on a convenient nail.

## PICK-UP TINES

Broken pick-up tines, if allowed to get into the cutting cylinder of a machine, can cause considerable damage. An idea which overcomes this danger is to wire each individual tine to the bar. Should the tine break or the securing bolt work loose the wire prevents it from falling on to the cutterbar and subsequently into the chopping mechanism.

## OUTSIDE LAMP

This idea for a cheap outside light comes from Mr. F. R. Hayllard, Lane Head Farm, Brough, Westmorland. It requires a screwlid preserve jar, **6 mm thick plastic disc, bulb holder and a square of 25 mm thick wood as a mounting block.**

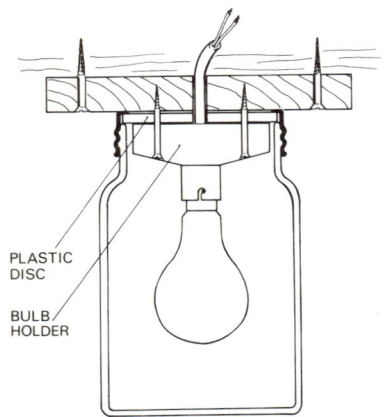

PLASTIC DISC

BULB HOLDER

First step is to remove the centre of the jar lid, leaving a lip for the plastic disc to grip. Then bore the holes through the disc to take the bulb holder screws and cable. Bore a 12 mm hole in the mounting block, connect up the cable and screw together. Keeping the bulbs under 100—150 watt will minimise any risk of heat damage to bulbs or fittings.

Several of these light units have been in use on Mr. Hayllard's farm for several years without trouble.

## BEET DRILLING: BAND SPRAYING

On light land, ideal beet drilling conditions often coincide with the March winds, which make band spraying unsafe.

Mr. R. L. Long, Fornham St. Martin, Suffolk, believes he has found the answer. By using inexpensive plastic household colanders he reduces the effect of the wind. The colanders simply screw on over the dust covers.

Mr. Long said he drilled his 52 ha of beet in record time when soil conditions were ideal, despite winds that would otherwise have prevented him from drilling.

## LOADER BUCKET

Dimensions. a (overall length) 1050 mm. b 115 mm. c (hole centres) 940 mm.

Quicker removal of accumulated spoil from alongside ditches is the aim of this idea from Mr. Donald Smith, Willow Grange, Stanfield, Dereham.

The loader bucket is held rigid in the working position by a stabilising bar made from two lengths of 30 mm x 100 mm channel iron, welded together to form a box section.

The weight of the bucket and loader frame gives adequate penetration to the cutting edge, even for scrub roots, claims Mr. Smith.

Although this example is for a M-F loader the idea could be applied to other makes.

## ESTIMATING SEED REQUIREMENTS PER ACRE

Mr. D. Thorne, West Panson, St. Giles, Cornwall, had difficulty in sowing the correct amount of grass seed an acre with his box-type drill. He made up a device out of an old bicycle wheel and forks and milometer operated by the spokes.

He fitted a small bracket to the rear of the drill and bolted the forks to the bracket to allow vertical movement of the forks so that the wheel kept on the ground.

He attached three strikers to the wheel spokes for accuracy and to lessen the effect of wheel slip over clods and hollows. The device has been in use and although not completely accurate, has been found far less wasteful on seed than estimation by eye.

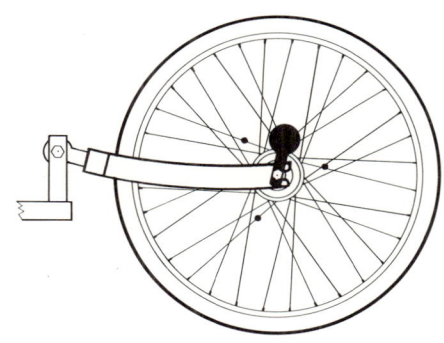

This bicycle wheel and milometer can be towed behind a seed drill to assist in estimating the quantity of seed to be sown per acre.

## PIN-HANDLE

Buckets, manure forks, and bale loaders often fit on to the same front-loader arms. But unless the tractor and attachment are both on a flat surface, lining up the holes on the frame with the holes on the attachment can be difficult, making it hard to push the pin into position. Get round this problem by welding a short handle to the flanged end of the pin. The handle will enable you to twist the pin and exert enough pressure to push into position even though the holes are not exactly in line.

### TRACTOR SERVICE PIPE CAP

The screw cover-cap which keeps dirt out of the tractor auxiliary services pipe is often lost when the pipe is connected to the tipping trailer or fore-end loader.

You can prevent loss by chaining the cap to the tractor. A 6 mm hole is drilled in the cap to take a bolt which holds the chain. The bolt is held fast by two lock-nuts, one inside and one outside the cap. The nuts are bronze welded to the cap to stop them working loose through vibration.

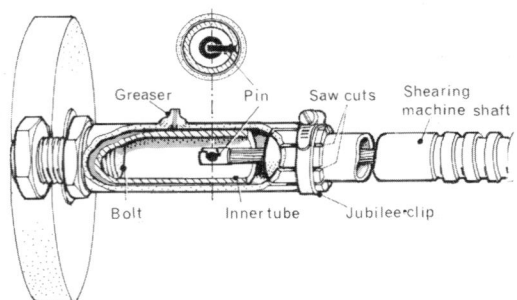

Greaser  Pin  Saw cuts  Shearing machine shaft

Bolt  Inner tube  Jubilee clip

### DOUBLE-USE SHEARER

Mr. C.E. Sands, Betws, Llangollen, has found out-of-season uses for a shearing machine. He uses an electric model with a grinding wheel or sanding disc in the workshop or a portable version for sharpening mower blades in the field. Two tubes fit one inside the other. The outer one has slits and a jubilee clip to enable it to grip the solid end of the shearing machine's flexible shaft.

The inner tube has a bolt welded to one end for mounting the grinder, and at the other a pin is welded so that it protrudes into the tube to clip on to the bayonet fitting on the end of the flexible shaft.

### AUTOMATIC TRIP FOR BALE SLEDGE

Remembering to trip the bale sledge at just the right time opposite the last heap of bales, keeping an eye on the crop feeding into the baler and navigating the tractor require a driver's full concentration.

Mr. N. H. F. Bish, Southwood Farm, Turham, Grantham, Lincs, has simplified the job by converting his bale sledge to automatic trip.

The trip arm (A) mounted on top of gate frame is supported by two bearings and has a short lever welded on to the rear edge. The

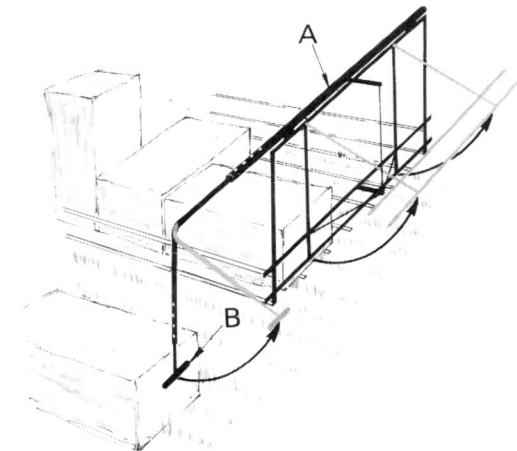

With slight modifications the attachment could be adopted for sledges with side hinged gates.

lever is connected to the gate release latch by a length of cord. When the striker arm (B) hits the heaps of bales dumped during the last round it rotates the trip arm which in turn automatically trips the gate latch.

The position of the striker arm may be altered laterally or vertically for varying crops or row widths or removed completely for transport.

## WELDING ON WHEELS

In many cases of machine breakdown on the farm gas welding equipment has to be taken to it to do a repair. This involves the inconvenience of wheeling the trolley long distances or heavy work lifting it on to a trailer for transport.

Mr. **Tyblewski, head of the machinery depart**ment at Northamptonshire College of Agriculture, fits the welding bottle trolley to the three-point linkage of a tractor.

He welded a bracket for the top link to the back of the trolley frame and repositioned the axle on the trolley so that when the wheels were taken off, the tractor linkage arms when lowered fitted on to the axle. He drilled the axle to take two spring clips that hold the arms on and to facilitate removal of the wheels.

The tractor is then backed up to the trolley, the trolley wheels are removed and the linkage fitted. Check chains must be tightened to prevent excess swaying, the gas turned off and the gauges removed from the bottles as jarring may upset their accuracy.

# COMING TO TERMS WITH HORSEPOWER

Horsepower is the most misunderstood word on the farm.

The term originally meant the amount of work one horse could do in a given time. Mechanically, however, an engine with more horsepower will not always pull more—it may only go faster. A car with a 70 kW engine will not necessarily pull a four-furrow plough even if the engine was in a tractor chassis. The factor which decides how much an engine will pull is the amount of TORQUE developed at the end of the crankshaft.

TORQUE is a rotating effort or the amount of force applied to the end of a crank arm multiplied by the length of the crank arm and measured in units called foot pounds. It can be explained simply as leverage; the longer the crank arm the more work achieved for the same force. Although many readers will have come to terms with metrication, others will still think in imperial units so these are used first to explain the meaning of horsepower.

If a force of 25lb is required to turn a socket brace with a crank arm length of 1ft one revolution, the torque is calculated as force x leverage, 25lb x 1ft = 25ft lb/torque. If the crank arm length was doubled more torque would result from the same force—25lb x 2ft = 50ft lb/torque.

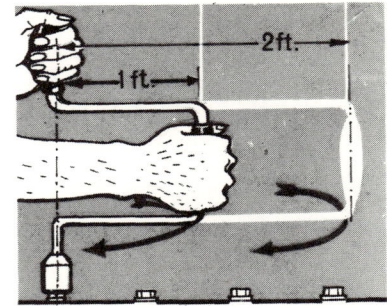

Doubling the lever doubles the torque and so on.

In an engine, the longer the crankshaft stroke the more torque is developed. A long-stroke engine has more pulling power than a short-stroke engine because the crankshaft has more leverage.

James Watt, inventor of the steam engine, found a good horse could hoist coal from a pit at an average rate of $366\frac{2}{3}$lb at 1ft per second or 22,000ft lb/per minute using the equation $366\frac{2}{3}$lb x 60 seconds. Watt took a few more factors into consideration and eventually arrived at a figure of 33,000ft lb/a minute and called this one horsepower.

So to arrive at a horsepower figure, the speed at which the force is applied must be included—horsepower=distance load moved in feet per minute x force in lb divided by 33,000.

Back to the man operating the socket brace, the distance his hand travels in one revolution is the circumference of a circle with 1ft radius which is 6.28ft. It he operated the brace at 50 rpm the horsepower (hp) developed would be

$$\frac{50 \text{ rpm} \times 6.28\text{ft} \times 25\text{lb}}{33,000} = 0.238$$

Indicated **hp** is the force exerted on the pistons multiplied by the length of stroke and rpm divided by 33,000. It is a theoretical figure and gives no real indication of the actual pulling power of an engine because up to 15 per cent can be used up in frictional losses before it gets to the flywheel. This means of expressing an engine's power is therefore not much good to the farmer as it does not tell him how much is available.

**Brake hp (bhp)** is the power developed at the flywheel as measured by a dynamometer on a test bed. A dynamometer is an instrument for measuring torque. Contrary to popular belief, it does not measure horsepower.

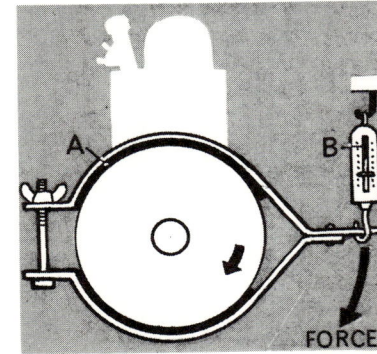

The diagram (page 42) shows a simplified dynamometer clamped round an engine flywheel it consists of a brake bank 'A' attached to a lever which is in turn connected to a measuring device 'B' to enable the force to be shown as lb. The same formula used to calculate the horsepower developed by the man using the socket brace is used to work out engine brake horsepower.

Brake hp is also subject to frictional losses before it eventually arrives at the point where it works for the farmer—hydraulic pumps, gear trains and various other accessories all absorb power. So that, as with indicated hp, not all brake hp is available for work.

Pto horsepower is the actual power available at the end of the splined shaft. Though measured in a similar way to bhp, the fact that it is at the end of the shaft means that no deductions have to be made for frictional losses and it is therefore a true hp rating.

Drawbar horsepower (dhp): next to pto hp, drawbar hp is the most useful figure to have. Another type of dynamometer is inserted between the tractor and the load to be pulled. The dynamometer shows the average pull in lb required to keep the load moving. This is multiplied by the forward speed and then divided by 33,000 hp to give dhp

$$\frac{\text{load in lb} \times \text{speed}}{33,000}$$

If the speed factor is in mph the formula becomes:

$$\text{dhp} = \frac{\text{load in lb} \times \text{speed}}{275}$$

The hp requirement to operate a plough demanding a pull of 2,000lb at 4 mph would be

$$\frac{2,000\text{lb} \times 4 \text{ mph}}{275} = 29\text{hp}$$

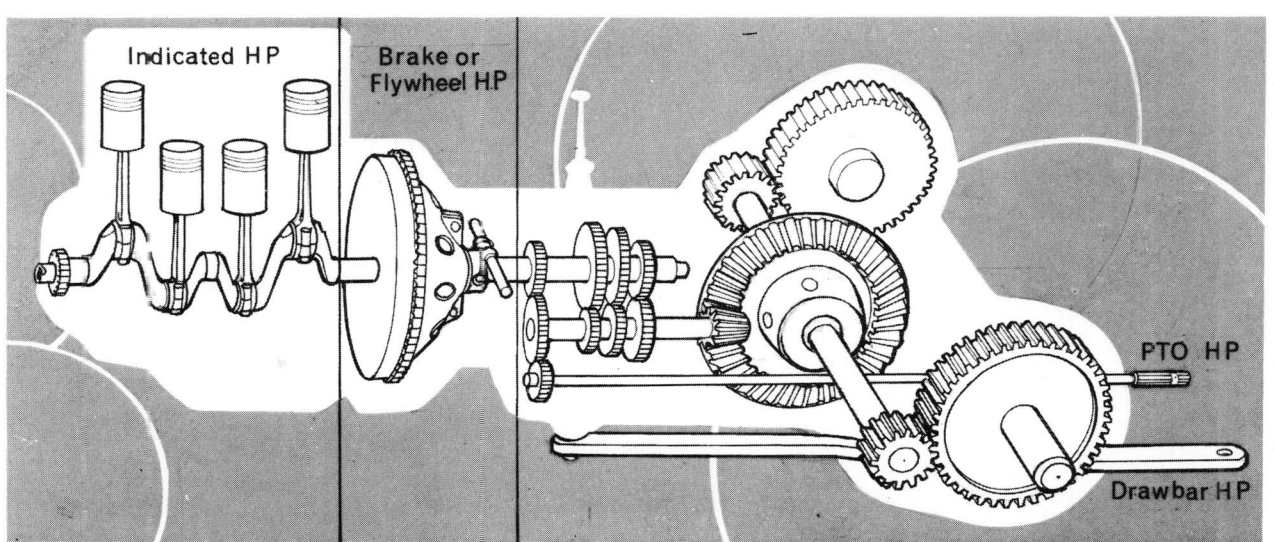

Indicated H P

Brake or Flywheel H.P.

PTO H P

Drawbar H P

Drawbar hp gives a real indication of a tractor's lugging ability. What really matters, however, is how many acres can be ploughed in a day, not how many furrows the tractor will pull. Pulling four 12in bodies at 5 mph will result in about two acres being ploughed in an hour. If the same tractor is overloaded with six 12in bodies working at 3 mph the work output drops to 1.8 acres an hour. The formula to use here is: acres per hour=

$$\frac{\text{working width in feet x mph}}{10}$$

Exactly the same logic follows when metric units are used. Pulling four 300 mm bodies at 8 km/h will result in about 1.0 ha being ploughed in an hour. If the same tractor is overloaded with six 300 mm bodies working at 4 km/h the work output drops to 0.7 ha an hour. The formula to use for working in metric units is: hectares per hour =

$$\frac{\text{working width in metres x km/h}}{10}$$

So when buying a new tractor or graduating to a bigger one make sure of the facts. Find out what horsepower is available for doing work and not just the power developed by the engine. When comparing the horsepowers compare like with like.

Rated horsepower is the brake-horsepower load an engine is capable of carrying for a period of 12 hours.

Continuous horsepower is the brake-horse-power load an engine is capable of carrying for continuous full-load runs of more than 24 hours.

Intermittent horsepower is the brake-horse-power load an engine is capable of carrying for short periods under varying loads.

Rated, continuous and intermittent hp figures are calculated on a test bed with engines fitted with full equipment, including radiator and fan.

Rated hp is usually around 90 per cent of maximum hp and continuous hp 90 per cent of rated hp.

In the case of metrication, the 'horse' is dropped and we simply talk about 'power' such as brake power or indicated power and change the units from horsepower to kilowatts. To convert, the equation is:

1 horsepower is equivalent to 746 watts.

The theory of power measured in kilowatts is, obviously, exactly the same as the theory of horse-power but the units of measurement are different right down to basics. Work is done when a force is applied to a body and the body moves in the direction of the force. The amount of *work done* is measured by the product:

force x distance moved by point of application of force

Thus, if a uniform force P moves a body a distance s measured in the direction of the force, then

work done by $P = P \times s$

If the force is in newtons and the distance in metres then the units of work are *newton metres.* A unit of work equal to one newton metre is defined in the SI system as the *joule* (J). The joule is defined precisely as *the work done when the point of application of a force of one newton is displaced through a distance of one metre in the direction of the force.*

*Power* is the rate of doing work. In the SI system the basic unit of power is the watt (W) which is defined as a rate of working equal to one joule per second, i.e. to the work done by a force of one newton in moving through a distance of one metre in one second. Thus

1 watt = 1 J/s = 1 Nm/s

You might reasonably go through the argument and then ask where the newton comes from. The newton is the SI standard of force and is defined as that force which, when applied to a body having a mass of one kilogram, gives it an acceleration of 1 metre per second per second (i.e. 1 m/s$^2$). So just as 'horsepower' came down to how fast a pound weight could be moved about so 'kilowatts' of power come down to how fast a kilogram can be moved.

# COMING TO TERMS WITH GEARS

Gears play an essential part in farm machinery, varying from the high quality types used in transmission systems to the cruder cast-iron ones used in corn drills and potato diggers.

The function of a gear is to transmit power smoothly from one shaft to another, and depending on the type and number of teeth, changes in speed, torque, direction of rotation and direction of drive can be made. For example, a tractor engine speed of 2,200 rpm can be reduced by gearing to give a rear wheel speed of 20 rpm. This enables tractors to develop high torque and good drawbar pull.

Gear efficiency is controlled by the design and accuracy of machining; a carefully manufactured gear-box should transmit power with a loss of less than 2 per cent per speed change.

Gears used to transmit heavy loads are hardened by special heat treatments and the materials used are constantly changing as new alloys are developed. For light work case-hardened steel or just plain cast-iron gears give sufficient strength.

When a number of gears are meshed together they are known as a gear train, and a number of gear trains working in conjunction with each other make up a power train.

Calculating the speed of a driven gear is made easy if the following formula is used:

rpm of driving gear x

$$\frac{\text{No of teeth in driving gear}}{\text{No of teeth in driven gear}}$$

There are many types of toothed gears and the difference between them lies in the arrangement of the teeth.

The spur, or straight tooth, gear is probably the most widely used and is the simplest form. The teeth are parallel to the centre line of the gear and can only be used where drive shafts are also parallel. When used in gear-boxes the teeth are chamfered to enable easier and smoother gear changing. Examples of spur gears can be found on most types of farm equipment.

Spiral gears are used to couple up shafts when the centre lines are not parallel. Contact between the teeth is confined to a single point, therefore, the load capacity is much less than that of spur or helical gears, where there is always a full line of contact between each pair of teeth as they mesh. For this reason, spiral gears are used for transmitting very light loads only.

The drive for tractormeters, speedometers and corndrill acremeters if often transmitted by this type of gear arrangement.

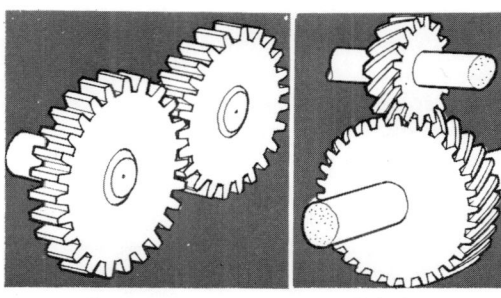

Spur gears.　　　　Spiral gears.

### RACK AND PINION

The rack and pinion is a variation of spur gearing, where one gear, the pinion, is a normal straight-toothed round gear and the rack is a straight-toothed flat gear. By mounting the pinion in fixed bearings and rotating it clockwise or anti-clockwise the rack can be made to move in either direction. This device is used in situations ranging from traversing a saw-bench platform to adjusting the amount of fuel delivered by an in-line injector pump.

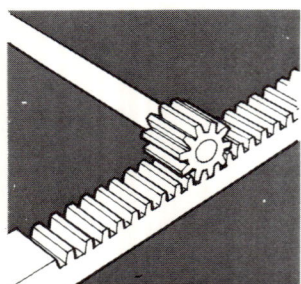

### WORM AND WHEEL

Worm and wheel gearing can be used for connecting shafts which are at right angles to one another and many early tractors used this method in the rear axle instead of bevel gears. The drive cannot be reversed; that is, the wheel cannot drive the worm. This made it impossible for tractors using this type of gearing to be tow-started.

Worm gears are especially useful when a big ratio of speed reduction is needed, for they can be designed to give a ratio of 70 to 1, whereas other types of gearing cannot easily give more than about 6 to 1 in any one pair.

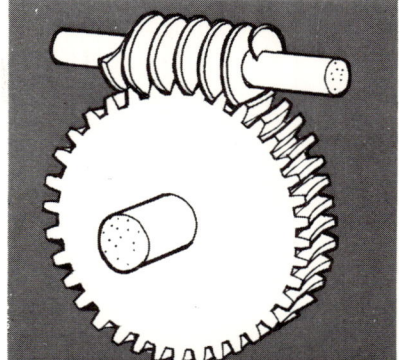

### BEVEL GEARS

Bevel gears are used to change the course of a drive through a right angle or when it is necessary to connect two shafts that are not parallel to each other, in which case they are called angle bevel gears.

Where smooth running is required, as in the differential of a tractor, the straight cut bevel gear tends to be unsuitable and a spiral bevel gear is used. The teeth each form part of a spiral and are matched to the teeth of the mating gear. Known commonly as a crown wheel and pinion, they are matched sets not interchangeable.

The adjustment of bevel gears in relation to each other is vital. Spur and helical gears have only one adjustment, backlash; but bevel gears have two, backlash and mounting distance. If incorrectly set noisy operations and excessive wear result.

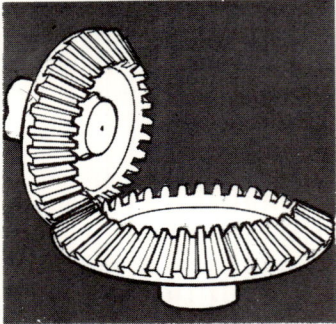

## HELICAL GEARS

Helical gears are used when smooth, quieter operation is needed, and they are fitted to many modern high-speed gearboxes. Although they have great strength and operate quietly at high speed, they have a disadvantage. When under load they tend to push each other sideways out of mesh, and in some cases special thrust bearings have to be provided to prevent this.

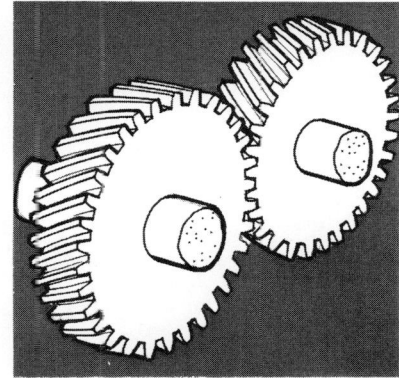

Helical

Double helical gears overcome the problem of sideways thrust, but have the disadvantage of not being able to slide in and out of mesh. The main application for this type of gear is for transmitting heavy loads.

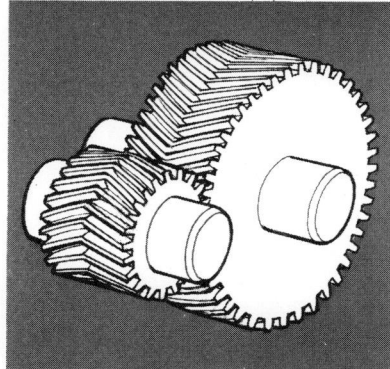

Double helical

## EPICYCLIC GEARING

Epicyclic gearing, or planetary gearing, provides a compact method of transmitting power, which may be arranged to give increases or reductions in speed.

The epicyclic principle is commonly used for rear axle final drive speed reduction and in transmission systems to give speed and torque amplification. Ford 'Dual Power' and Massey Ferguson 'Multipower' adopt epicyclic gearing to obtain speed changes on the move without have to declutch.

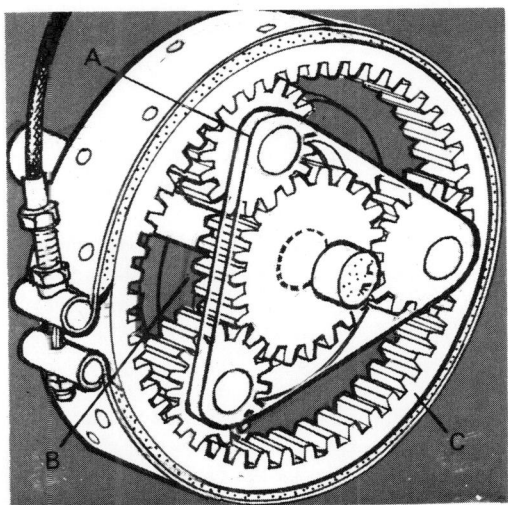

Above is shown the working principle of a two-speed epicyclic unit.

If the ring gear (C) is allowed to revolve the whole assembly turns as one unit, the speed of the output sun gear (B), being the same as the input planet carrier (A). When the ring gear is held stationary by a brake the planet carrier is made to rotate within the ring gear. This, in turn, speeds up the sun gear and increases the output speed.

# COMING TO TERMS WITH HYDRAULICS

The power output of a tractor can be delivered
at three points: drawbar, pto shaft and hydraulic
system. To date tractor capabilities have been
measured in terms of dhp and pto hp performance
only. But with the development of sophisticated
hydraulic linkage systems and hydrostatic trans-
missions the need for a greater understanding of
how they work and how to get the best performance increases every day.

Hydraulics is the science of fluid forces and
through modern usage it has come to mean the
use of fluid (usually oil) to transfer or change a
source of power into usable power.

In the seventeenth century a scientist called
Pascal discovered the basic law upon which
modern hydraulics work. The law is: if a pressure
is applied at any point in a static fluid it will be
the same in all directions and acts with equal
force on equal areas (Fig.1).

Fluids are almost incompressible and because
of this forces may be transmitted, increased and
controlled by means of a fluid under pressure.

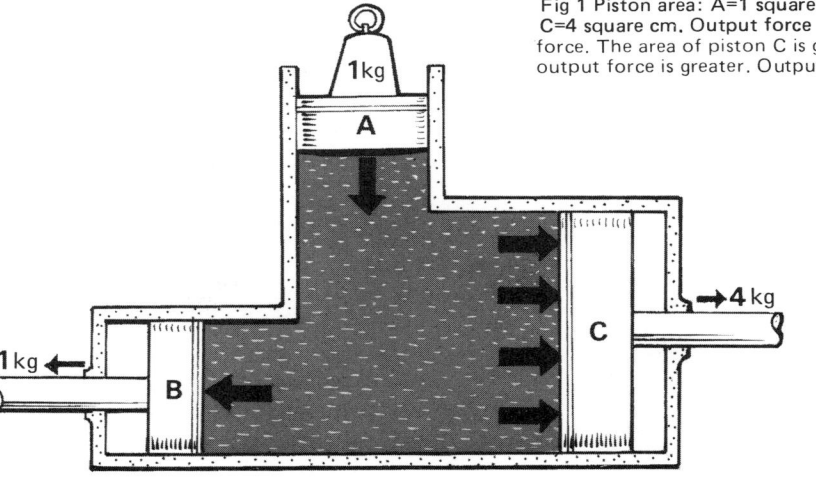

Fig 1 Piston area: A=1 square cm B=1 square cm and
C=4 square cm. Output force from B is equal to input
force. The area of piston C is greater, therefore the
output force is greater. Output is proportional to input.

All hydraulic systems, whether a simple single-acting ram for operating a combine pick-up reel or a 100kW tractor with draught control and hydrostatic transmission, use fundamental design features (Fig 2).

If a force of 1 kg is exerted on piston A and moves it 100 mm down its cylinder, 100 x 100 = 10,000 cubic mm of oil will be displaced if the area of cross section of the piston is 100 sq mm. The displaced oil will be forced against the 1000 sq mm face of ram B and lift the load of 10 kg by 10 mm. This is calculated by dividing the oil displaced by the area of the piston B. The pressure under A and B must be the same, so if B has 10 times the area it will lift 10 times as much but will do so through only 1/10 the distance.

To convert the simple systems shown above into a workable hydraulic system it is necessary to incorporate a pump, two non-return valves—one on the inlet side of the pump and one on the output side—and an oil reservoir.

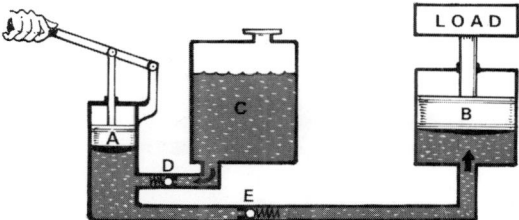

A Hand pump. B Lift cylinder. C Reservoir. D and E Non-return valves.

Any force developed by the hand pump (A) will exert a greater force on the piston (B) according to the multiplication forces (area of piston x distance piston moved).

To move the piston through a complete stroke it is necessary to have a reservoir to supply the extra oil required. Non-return valves permit the oil to be pumped from the reservoir, which is at atmospheric pressure, to the cylinder at increased pressure.

The oil pumped into the cylinder (B) cannot return to the reservoir so it is necessary to connect a directional control valve and a return pipe (see diagram on next page).

As most systems require a continuous oil flow the left hand pump is replaced with a motor-driven pump and a pressure relief valve (prv) is fitted. Without a prv the pump would have to be stopped at the exact moment the piston reached the end of its travel or when the valve was closed.

Fig. 2 Area of piston A = 100 square mm, Area of piston B = 1000 square mm.

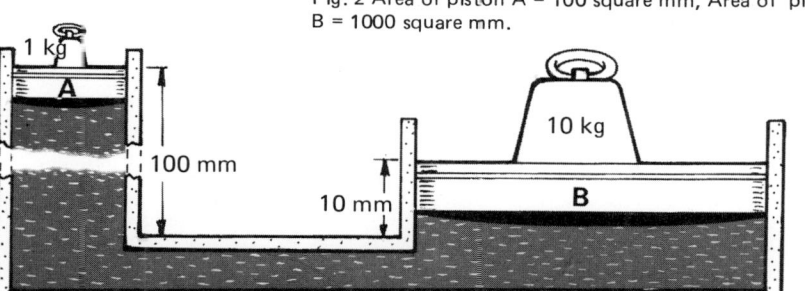

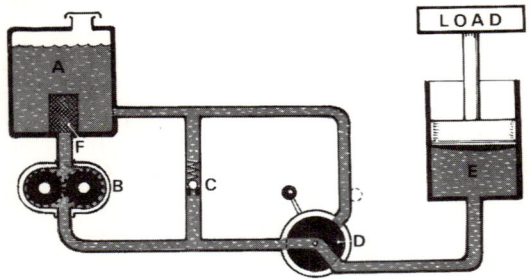

A Reservoir. B Pump. C Non-return valve D Directional control valve. E Lift cylinder. F Filter.

If the pump were not stopped the pressure would keep building up to the point where seal and hoses would rupture. Relief valves are usually set to a predetermined pressure.

Ease of control is one of the big advantages of hydraulic power. The flow and pressure can be altered to give stepless speed changes and lifting capacities. It may be routed through flexible hoses or piped, thus doing away with the complicated systems required for mechanical drives.

Hydraulic power is efficient and cheap to operate, small forces are able to handle much larger loads, losses through friction are small, automatic lubrication reduces wear on moving parts, the system is very flexible in respect of the positioning of components, and speed can be easily controlled.

The power for a hydraulic system is supplied by the pump, and the external gear type is most commonly used for farm equipment.

It operates on the principle that as the gears revolve, oil trapped between the gear teeth and the housing is carried from the suction side to the outlet side of the pump, one gear being driven and the other following (see diagram below).

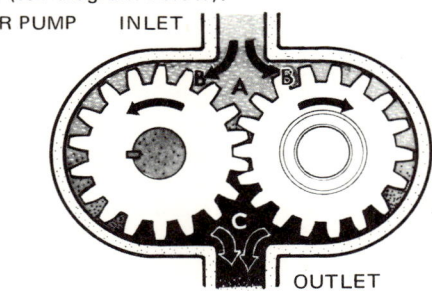

Wear in gears and housing reduces efficiency.

Efficiency is determined by the relation and closeness of fit of the working parts.

Straight cut spur gears are often used, but helical gears (see page 47) are sometimes used to give smoother operation and slightly higher pressure.

Other types of pumps include internal gear, screw, vane centrifugal and reciprocating piston. These may be classified into two operational types—fixed or constant delivery, or variable delivery.

The variable type is not used as often as the constant delivery because it is more expensive to manufacture and more complex. It is usually restricted to applications where variable delivery is a necessity.

Clearances in hydraulic pumps are critical and the smallest particle of dirt can result in operating problems. Excessive wear, for example, causes internal slippage of the oil within the pump. This is internal leakage from the high pressure side of the pump and will reduce output and increase oil temperature.

When the gears in the pump part (A) a slight suction is created, which assists in drawing in oil from the reservoir. The oil is then picked up by the gear teeth (B) and carried to the outlet side of the pump. As the teeth engage (C) they displace oil and force it through the outlet port.

Hydraulic power can be calculated by multiplying the oil pressure in bar by the flow rate in litres/min and multiplying by $13.6 \times 10^{-4}$

$$\text{i.e. kW} = \frac{\text{bar} \times \text{litres/min} \times 13.6}{10,000}$$

Vane pumps can deliver large quantities of oil at relatively high pressures. Wear does not greatly affect efficiency because the vanes can move in their slots to maintain contact with the housing. But dirt can cause the vanes to seize and reduce efficiency.

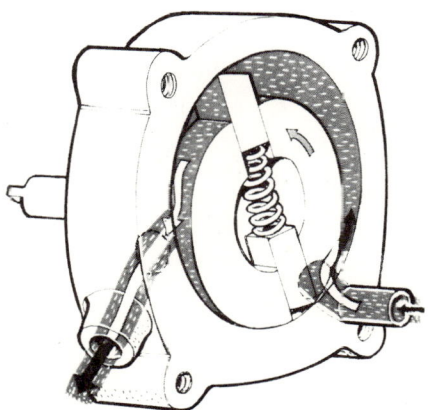

The rotor is mounted eccentrically to the housing.

## HYDRAULIC CYLINDERS

Hydraulic cylinders, or rams as they are more commonly called, are most popular for converting hydraulic power into work.

They may be either single acting (S/A) or double acting (D/A), depending on the application.

A S/A cylinder relies on the weight of the load to return the piston to its home position, whereas the D/A type is under pressure in both directions.

It is important that D/A cylinders are fitted the right way round. The piston area at one end is greater than the other because of the space taken up by the piston rod (see diagram below right).

This results in a slower more powerful upward stroke and a faster less powerful downward stroke providing the pressure is the same at both ends.

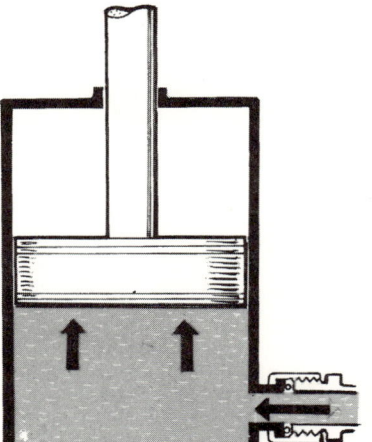

A single acting cylinder

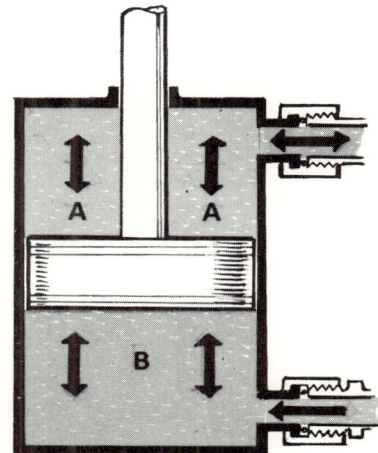

A double acting cylinder showing how piston area A is less than area B.

# TRACTOR FUEL SYSTEMS

## HOW TO SERVICE THEM

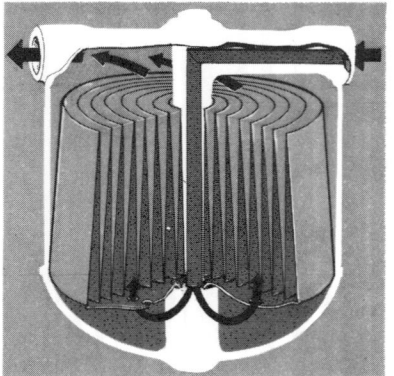

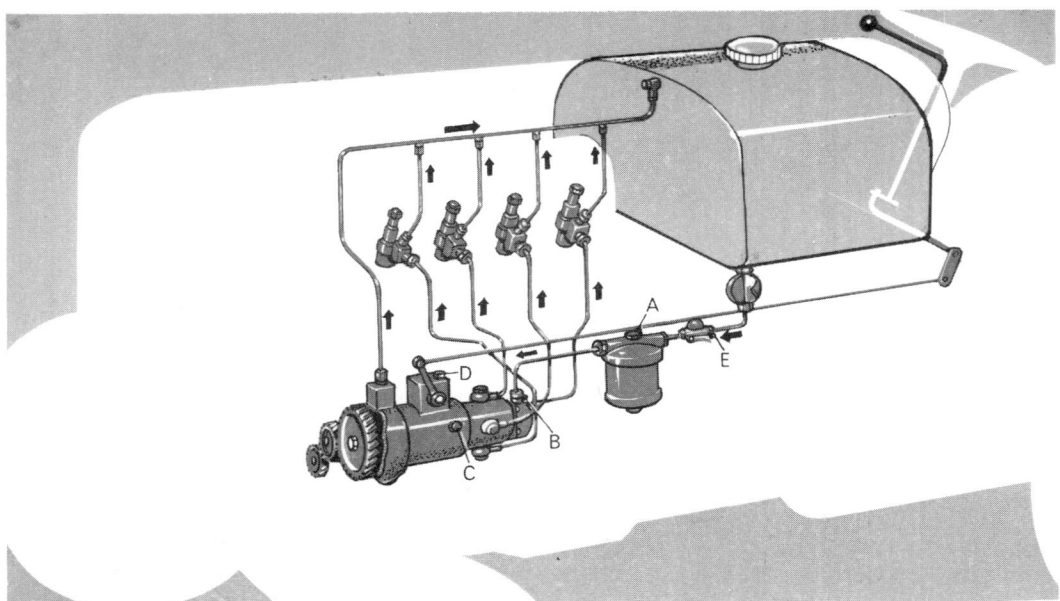

The fuel filter's job is to remove dust and dirt particles which could damage and speed up wear of pump barrels and plungers. It can filter a large volume of fuel without choking or causing a resistance in the fuel flow. There are various types but the most common is the paper element in a canister. The paper strips wound round a cylindrical core in a spiral are welded together at the top and bottom to form a series of continuous v-shaped coils. The paper used is resin treated and 'creped' for strength.

If any part is removed, or if the system runs out of fuel, air enters and the system must be vented. Venting points are usually shown in the operator's manual. The system shown in the drawing would be vented as follows:
(1)  Ensure that there is an adequate supply of fuel and that the engine stop control is in the running position.
(2)  Loosen union A on top of the filter.
(3)  Operate the hand priming lever on the feed pump E until fuel flows free from air bubbles, then tighten the union while the fuel is still flowing.
(4)  Loosen the inlet pipe B at the injector pump and repeat operation 3.
(5)  Loosen the lower vent screw C and repeat operation 3.
(6)  Loosen the upper vent screw D and repeat operation 3.
(7)  Set the throttle lever to the fully open position and slacken all injector unions.
(8)  Turn the engine on the starter motor a few times then tighten the injector unions.
(9)  Start the engine. If it runs unevenly slacken one injector union for a few seconds then re-tighten.

## TRACTOR FUEL SYSTEMS

The fuel system supplies a tractor's life blood at the right time and in the correct quantity—if it is working efficiently. If it is not, output suffers and tempers get frayed.

A drop of water or a speck of dust is enough to upset the balanced supply and the trouble may be found in the supply tank, the injectors, the pump, the filter, or anwhere in between.

Fuel systems can vary in layout and design according to the make of tractor but all have an injector pump incorporating some form of governor, injectors, feed pump, filters and/or a water trap and a fuel reservoir.

Repair or adjustment of the more complicated mechanisms like the injectors or pump is not usually a job for the farm workshop, but keeping the rest of the system in trim is.

The importance of clean fuel is not always sufficiently appreciated. Dirt, particularly fine dust carried in the air, is the main enemy of the diesel engine.

Tractors often work in 'dust-bowl' conditions and trouble-free operation depends on clean fuel. The injection pump, the 'heart' of an engine, and the injector nozzles which spray the fuel into the cylinders are precision made with high-finished surfaces. Abrasion from dust and dirt in the fuel can soon ruin their efficiency. As little as 0.003 mm or 30 microns wear of the mating surfaces in critical parts can stop it working.

A point to remember is that the manufacturer's warranty does not apply if failure is due to dirt or water getting in.

Regular day-to-day maintenance pays. The first thing a good horseman did when he finished work for the day was to rub down and feed his horse. Why not treat the tractor with the same care.

Do not drive the tractor into its shed and leave it until next morning when time for maintenance cannot be spared. Do it then. Keeping the fuel tank full helps prevent the build up of condensation. Even so a certain amount of condensation will form so keep an eye on the water tap and drain it regularly.

Look for fuel leaks. This may mean giving the engine a rub down, for leaks often go undetected because the engine and injection equipment are covered in dirt. Finally make a note of anything that occurred during the day that might mean trouble.

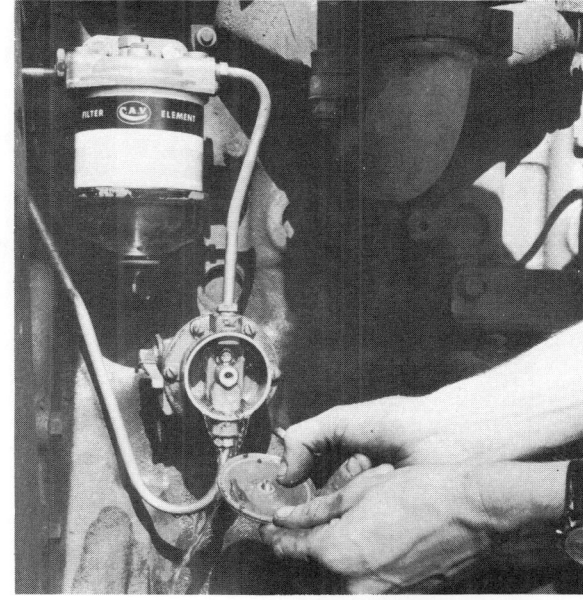

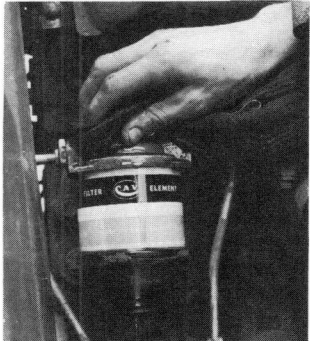

Fuel feed pump servicing: remove the cover and gauze strainer (if fitted) and clean out any sediment that may have collected. Replace the gauze and cover, then vent the system.
(*Right*) Some systems have a water trap to collect any condensation in the fuel. Water, being heavier than fuel, accumulates at the bottom of the trap and should be drained off at least once a week. The bowl should be removed periodically and cleaned.

## INJECTION PUMPS

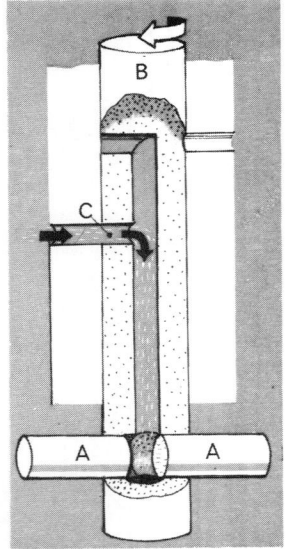

Fig. 1 Rotary pump—induction stroke, plungers separated.

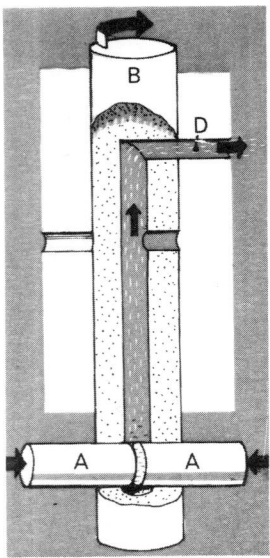

Fig. 2 Rotary pump—injection stroke, plungers together.

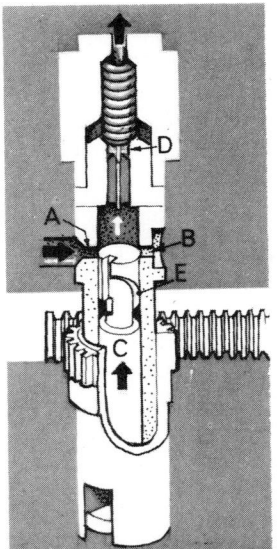

Fig. 3 In-line pump element— starting injection stroke.

The injection pump meters fuel and injects it at high pressure into the combustion chambers at the correct time. Both types of pump in use today—distributor rotary and in-line—produce the same result.

The pumping action of the rotary type is produced by two plungers (A) worked by a cam ring.

As the rotor (B) turns one of the inlet ports (C) opens and fuel enters the rotor separating the plungers (Fig 1). As the rotor turns the inlet port closes, the distributor port (D) comes into line with one of the fuel outlets, and the plungers are forced towards each other to form the injection stroke (Fig 2). Fuel trapped between the plungers

is forced back through the rotor to the injector.

When the plungers reach the limit of inward travel the distributor port closes, sealing off the fuel line to injector and the cycle repeats itself, sending fuel through each outlet in turn. This pump can be fitted horizontally or vertically and is lubricated by the fuel.

The in-line type has separate elements for each engine cylinder instead of the single pump barrel and plungers of the rotary type. Each element (Fig 3) has a cam-driven plunger sliding in a barrel sealed at the top by a spring-loaded delivery valve. The inlet port (A) is connected to a gallery running the length of the pump, which is kept full with fuel at a constant pressure. Opposite the inlet port is a spill port (B) through which excess fuel can drain away.

As the plunger (C) descends the ports open and fuel flows into the space above the plunger, which pressurises it as it rises. The delivery valve (D) is forced off its seat and fuel flows at high pressure to the injector. This continues until the upper edge of the helix (E) in the plunger is open to the spill port, when pressure is suddenly released by fuel escaping down the groove in the plunger and out through the spill port, the delivery valve closes and injection ends.

The injector pump is a complicated piece of equipment and repairs and adjustments should be left to the experts, who have all the up-to-date information and special tools.

## INJECTORS

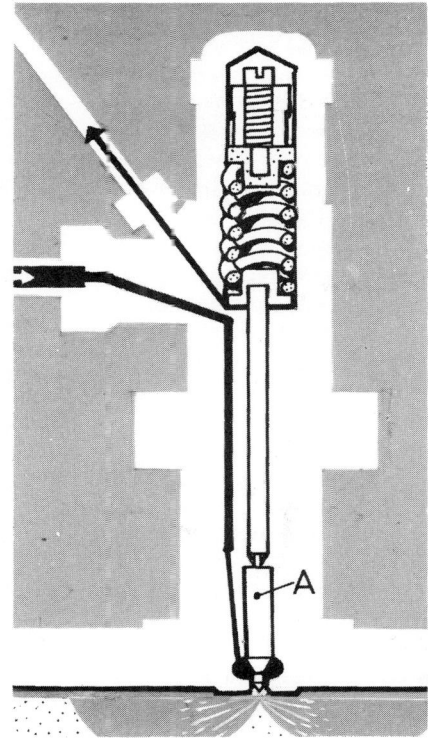

Power output of a diesel engine is governed to a great extent by the efficiency of the injectors. Before maximum power can be obtained from the fuel injected into the cylinders, it must be atomised to allow it to mix freely with the air. This is the job of the nozzles fitted to the end of each injector.

Various types are used, depending on the design of engine, the two main types being hole nozzles and pintle nozzles.

The hole nozzle may have two, three or four equally spaced holes through which the fuel is forced out in fine sprays (2). These holes can just be seen by the naked eye, which underlines the need for clean fuel. One blocked hole can cause a loss of up to 2 kW.

The pintle nozzle does the same job, but instead of the fuel being sprayed out of a number of holes, it is emitted as a single conical spray (3).

Hole nozzles normally are used for direct injection engines and pintle for indirect. They have to withstand high pressures ranging from 100 to 200 atmospheres (100 to 200 bar) and from 150 to 1,500 injections a minute, depending on the rated engine speed.

(1) shows the working principle of the injector. Fuel, under pressure from the pump, forces the spring loaded needle valve 'A' from its seat and emerges as an atomised spray. As soon as the delivery pressure falls off, the spring returns the valve to its seat.

Symptoms of inefficient operation can be intermittent misfiring one or more cylinders; smoky exhaust—black smoke indicating an injector discharging unvaporised fuel and blue smoke indicating a partially blocked injector; pronounced knock in one or more cylinders; increased fuel consumption; engine overheating or loss of power.

**1** Working principles of the injector

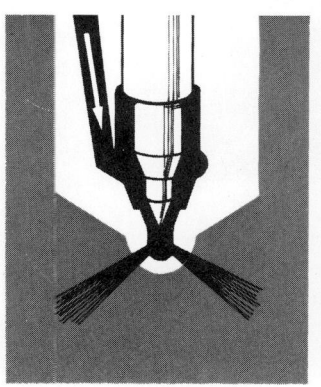

**2** Multi-hole nozzle

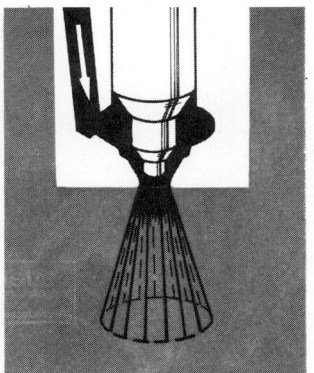

**3** Pintle-type nozzle

1

2

## CHANGING FUEL INJECTORS

Fuel injectors should be changed every 600 hours. Failure to do so will result in excessive wear, giving poor engine performance and heavier fuel consumption. Injectors cost only a few pounds for a reconditioned set of four and it is not worth trying to get an extra few hours of use from them.

Ensure that you get the correct replacements. If a reconditioned set is obtained before removal of those to be changed, the dealer will want to know the tractor serial number and the engine serial number.

Strict cleanliness must be observed throughout the operation. Carefully blow, or wash off with paraffin and brush, all dust and dirt from around the injectors (1). A certain amount of dismantling may be necessary prior to this; certain tractors require removal of the fuel tank.

Turn off the fuel if the tank was not removed in step one and remove leak-off pipes and high-pressure fuel delivery pipes. It may be necessary to drain some fuel from the tank where it has not been removed, as some leak-off pipes are directly connected to the tank and fuel may leak back. Better still, tackle the job when the tank is nearly empty. Slacken off the pipes at the pump end also, to avoid bending them when removing the pipes from the injectors (2). Slacken the injector retaining nuts and pull the injectors from their recess. If they are tight use a large open-ended spanner, push one jaw under the lug of the injector and give the other end a sharp blow with the palm of the hand. This should be sufficient to loosen the injector (3).

Pick out the copper seating washer with a screwdriver or file tang. Clean carbon from the recess with a blunt screwdriver, then turn the engine over on the starter, to blow out any particles from the cylinders.

Fit new copper washer, place the new injector on its retaining studs and tighten the nuts evenly. If this is not done evenly, the injector will not seat properly and the compression of the engine will blow the fuel past the injector, resulting in poor performance.

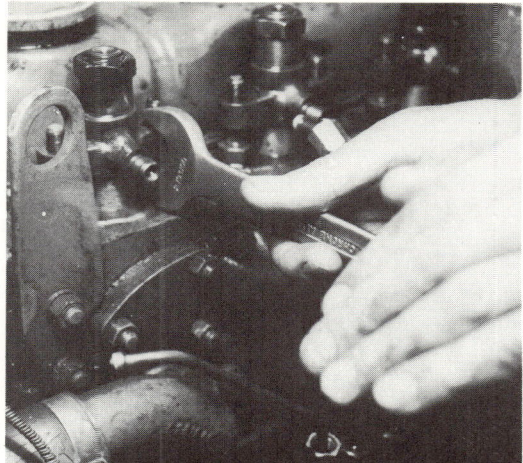

**3**

Connect up all fuel pipes, making sure all the olives on the pipes are seated properly to obviate leaks. Replace the leak-off pipes, fitting new copper or aluminium washers where required (4). and turn on the fuel. Bleed the system of air, start the engine and check for leaks.

If diesel fuel affects your hands—it can cause dermatitis—apply a good barrier cream beforehand and wash your hands thoroughly in soapy water when the job has been completed.

## SAFE REPAIR FOR A LEAKING FUEL TANK

The repair of large fuel tanks is not a job for the non-professional, but small tanks may be soldered, without undue difficulty, after thorough cleaning.

Such tanks may be accidentally dented and though the impact may not cause a leak a rust

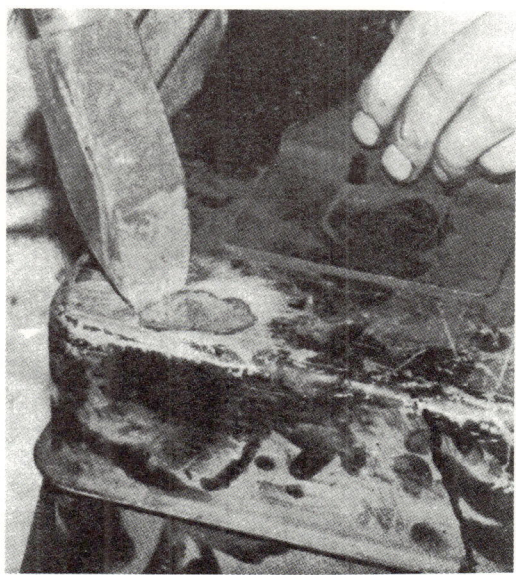

After covering the iron tip and damaged area with flux, tin both liberally with solder.

patch might form and eat through the metal. In these cases, and where a leak has developed as a direct result of mechanical damage, the soldering method can effect a speedy and efficient repair.

First, the tank must be completely cleaned. It should be emptied and inverted to drain before being thoroughly washed out—preferably with hot water. Allow to dry and check for fuel odours before either washing out again or starting the

repair. The damaged area must be scraped and wire-brushed down to bare metal.

Following the sequence illustrated will result in a sound job. Do not attempt to weld or braze a fuel tank of any kind using a naked flame.

Afterwards scrub the outside under a hot tap to remove surplus flux; flush the inside with paraffin.

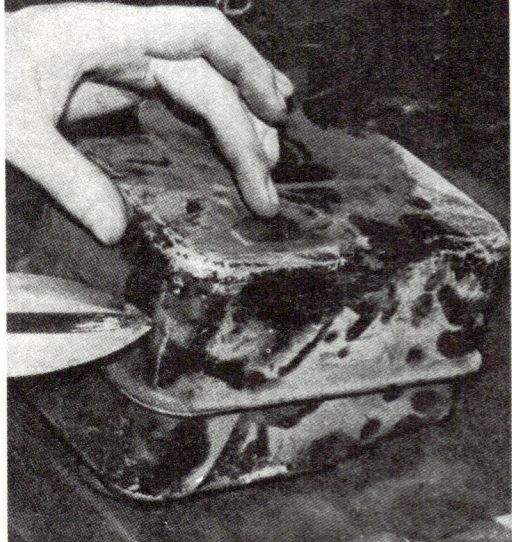

Cut a small piece of sheet steel to cover the damage. Clean it with emery cloth and tin one side.

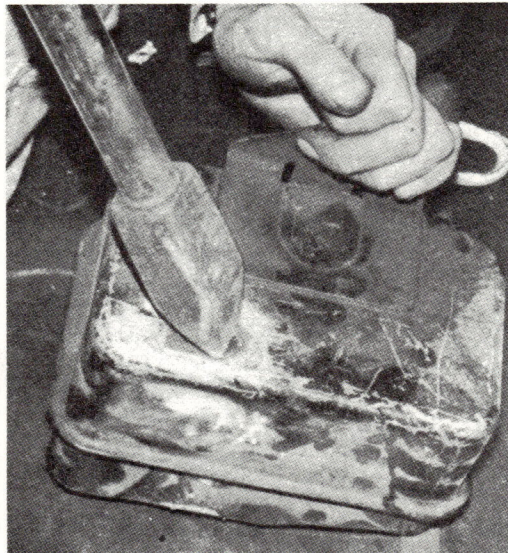

Place the steel plate over the repair and press it with the soldering iron to sweat it on.

## TRACTORS: LUBRICATION

The main object of an engine's lubrication system is to reduce the amount of friction and wear in the bearings and other moving parts.

No matter how smooth a bearing surface may be, a lack of oil to lubricate it will result in rapid wear, overheating and loss of power.

It does its job by maintaining a thin film of oil between rubbing surfaces, such as big and small end bearings and on the piston rings sliding up and down inside their cylinders, and by cushioning the combined sliding rolling action of gear teeth. Oil forms a seal between the piston rings and cylinder walls to reduce compression losses and also helps to keep the engine cool.

Oil may be distributed to the working parts of an engine by either splash or forced circulation.

The splash system (see drawing) is only used for the less complicated and slower running engines and works by allowing the ends of the connecting rods to dip into oil troughs fitted across the crankcase. As they hit the oil at speed, a fine spray is formed within the crankcase and oil is splashed on to cylinders, connecting rod small end, bearings and tappets.

The big end bearings get their supply from small scoops (A) fitted to the end of each big end bearing cap. These scoops pick up oil and feed it direct into the bearing through a communicating hole in the cap. Oil for the remaining

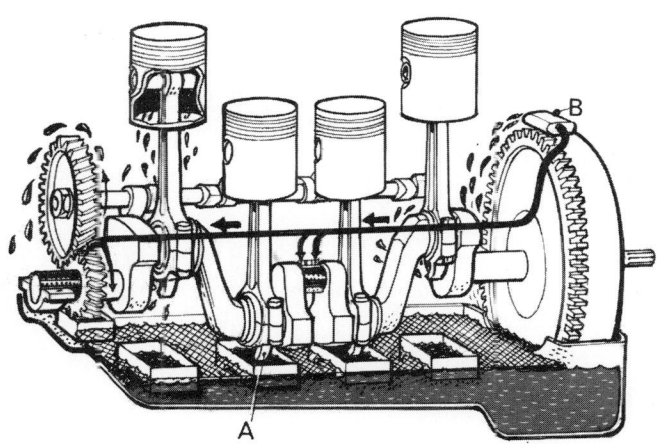

The splash system, shown in the drawing, is used for less complicated and slower running engines. The big end bearings get their supply from the scoops (A). Oil for other parts is fed into a funnel ended pipe (B).

parts is usually drawn out of the sump by the flywheel and fed into the funnel-ended pipe (B) which distributes it to such parts as main crankshaft bearings and timing gears.

The splash system relies on the amount of oil in the troughs and will only operate efficiently if the sump contains the correct amount.

A high-speed engine naturally requires a greater quantity of oil and it has to be distributed more positively. Engines fitted to modern tractors are usually rated at speeds ranging from 2,000 rpm to 2 500 rpm and a splash system would be grossly inadequate. For these engines, forced circulation is necessary.

Engines with forced circulation systems are fitted with a pump which sucks oil from the sump and delivers it under pressure to all bearings and by spray or drip feed to the other assemblies.

The pressure at which the oil circulates depends largely on the type and design of the engine. This is usually around 3.5 to 4.0 bar and high-low pressure limits are usually shown on a gauge.

The pipes and borings which distribute the oil vary, but the basic principles are always the same. The drawing shows a forced circulation oil system applicable to most engines.

The oil picked up by the pump is first fed into the main gallery (A) then routed by separate pipes or borings to the main crankshaft bearings (B). Next it is pumped through oilways bored through the centre of the crankshaft to each big end bearing (C) and oil surplus to requirement is forced out as a fine spray to lubricate the cylinder walls. A small hole drilled in the connecting rods from the big end bearings gives the small ends their supply.

The rocker shaft and valve gear is fed by a pipe (D) leading from the main gallery (A). This pipe usually has a **restrictor valve to control**

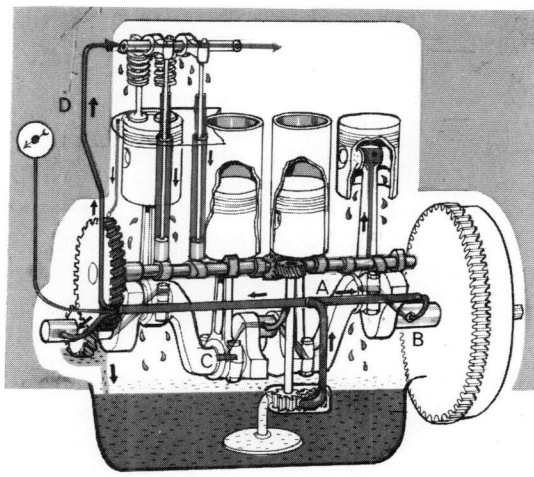

The forced circulation system, shown in the drawing, is necessary for high speed engines to give more positive oil distribution.

the amount of oil pumped to the rocker chamber and prevent flooding the top of the engine. As this oil drains back into the sump it is directed on to the camshaft timing gears and push-rods.

It is not critical to keep an exact oil level in a forced system, but it should be checked after a day's work.

If the oil gauge registers a reading above or below normal operating pressure when the engine is warm, stop immediately. On a cold morning the gauge will read slightly higher than normal because the oil is thicker.

By keeping the engine clean a leak is easily seen and the fault remedied. A leak at the rate of a drop every half-minute, which may not be obvious, will cost about a gallon of oil a month.

An engine must have good quality clean oil if it is to perform satisfactorily. If metal particles, carbon deposits and dust are allowed to accumulate they mix with the oil and form an abrasive compound, which increases the wear in bearings and piston rings.

Once rings become worn their effectiveness is reduced, causing poor compression and inefficient fuel burning. This further increases contamination and is the beginning of a vicious circle.

Generally speaking, the life of an oil is affected more by dirt contamination than by any other factor, so it is necessary to have an efficient filter—full-flow or by-pass—between the pump and the lubrication system.

The full-flow version filters all the oil delivered by the pump and discharges it direct into the system, whereas the by-pass takes only a small amount at a time—8-10 per cent—and returns it to the sump.

By-pass filters, on the whole, remove a larger proportion of dirt from the oil than full-flow filters, and many engine manufacturers prefer them.

Because the full-flow has to handle more oil, it is usually larger and coarser.

Material used to make filters includes cotton, felt and paper and it is false economy to try to clean them, just as it is to extend the recommended oil change period.

When changing a filter element avoid dislodging the deposits inside it into the oil system.

The pump, the power unit of the lubrication system, has to supply a constant flow of oil at correct pressure into a network of pipes and oilways.

It is generally fitted low enough in the sump to be completely submerged in the oil and is driven by a vertical shaft and spiral gears from the camshaft.

FULL FLOW FILTER

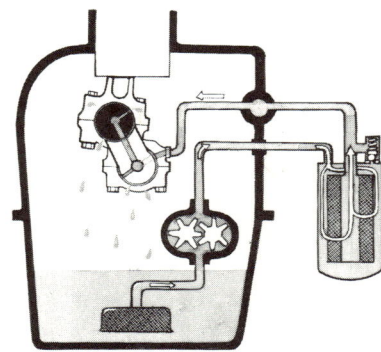

All the oil delivered by the pump is filtered

BY-PASS FILTER

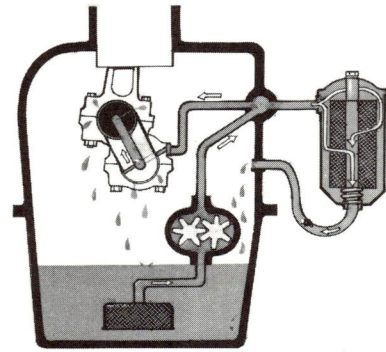

Only a small amount of oil is filtered at a time

Modern pumps are designed to deliver more oil than is required. Flow and pressure are controlled by a pressure relief valve (prv), usually incorporated in the pump body. The valve is preset to open as soon as the designed pressure is exceeded, and adjusts automatically, so that the pressure will not be affected by normal wear.

To maintain constant pressure a positive delivery pump is necessary and most commonly used is the gear and rotary-vane type.

The gear pump (1) consists of a driver spur gear (A) meshing with an idler gear (B) within a close-fitting housing. The oil sucked in is carried round by the teeth and pressurised when they mesh, thus being forced out through the delivery port (C). The amount of oil delivered is dictated by the speed at which the pump is driven.

The vane pump (2), is not as widely used. It consists of a rotor (A) which turns inside an eccentric housing (B). Two or more spring-loaded vanes (C), depending on the capacity required, are slotted into the rotor and, as it revolves, the ends of the vanes wipe against the housing walls. Oil is sucked in during one half revolution and pumped out during the other half.

Dust and grit get into the oil by way of the air intake and crankcase breather pipe. These small particles tend to be held in suspension in the oil and, if not removed, will cause wear to the pump mechanism and block up the oilways. It is, therefore, necessary to insert a filter.

The oil pump inlet usually has its own strainer, which is purely a primary filter of fine mesh gauze. The pump filter was at one time a gauze tray, but on modern engines it is more likely to be saucer shaped and mounted to a floating intake pipe, which rises and falls with the oil level. This draws oil from just below the surface and not from the bottom of the sump, where most of the sediment collects.

To say that oil makes a bearing surface slippery and reduces friction is only half the answer. A crankshaft, for example, floats within its bearing just as a boat floats on water. Remove the oil and direct metal to metal contact will soon wear

A gear pump in situ shlowing the prv spring gears and hinged filter screen.

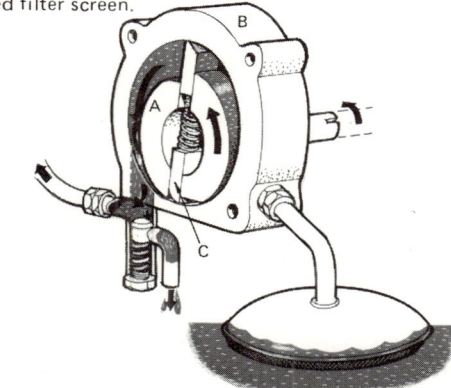

(1) Left: The gear pump, (2) Right: The vane pump.

it out. Oil must also be capable of coping with other factors and chemical changes.

One problem facing lubrication engineers is 'cold-start corrosion.'

Fuel burned within an engine produces a considerable amount of water, some of which is exhausted as steam or in drops. The remainder mixes with the combustion gases and forms acids which eat into the cylinder walls. Engine wear is greater just after starting. When correct working temperature is reached the acids cease to be dangerous, being vaporised and exhausted.

Oxygen combined with oil, especially in mist form in the crankcase, causes oxidation, discolouring and thickens the oil. The action forms carbon and soot which get into the thickened oil and form sludge. This picks up fine particles of metal and dust and if oil is not changed periodically oilways may become blocked and wear speeded up. Dirty oil can cause sticking piston rings and damage to valves, leading to excessive fuel consumption. Additives help.

Oil surrounds the bearings a, b, and c so that they 'float.'

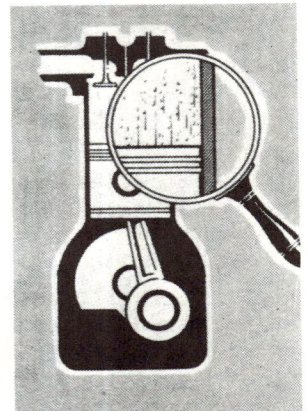
Moisture combines with combustion gases to form acids which eat into the cylinder walls.

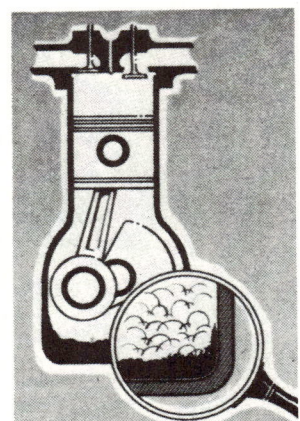
Oxygen combining with the oil causes oxidation which discolours and thickens the oil.

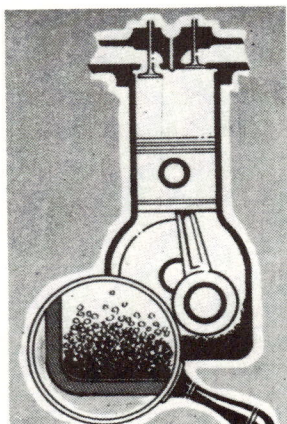
Without the bubble-pricking action of antifoam additives a crankcase would soon be a mass of foam.

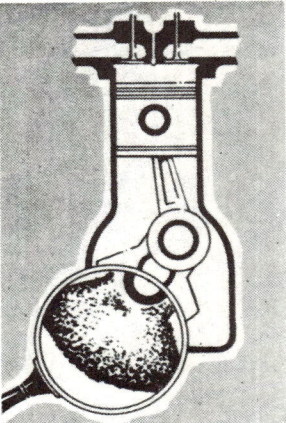
Carbon and soot formation produces sludge and sticky deposits—answer, regular oil changes.

## ADDITIVES AND VISCOSITY

Additives—tailor-made chemical compounds added to an oil to improve an existing property or give it an additional one—include:

Anti-oxidant. Combats oxidation by preventing oil combining with oxygen to form harmful materials.

Detergent dispersant. Keeps engines free from lacquer deposits which form at high temperatures and sludges which form at low temperatures. Impurities and fine particles are kept separate by suspending them in oil.

Anti-wear. Improves lubrication by increasing oil's resistance to being pushed out of a bearing when under pressure.

Anti-rust additives. Beneficial where engines are not used regularly and are therefore prone to rusting. Provide protective coating on engine interior.

Anti-foam. Prevents oil foaming in crankcase.

Viscosity Index (VI) Improver. Viscosity index measures how much an oil thins when heated. High VI oils thin more than low VI oils. A VI improver is inactive when the oil is at low temperatures but slows down the thinning process at high temperatures (see graph).

Viscosity is measured by a viscometer, which consists basically of a metal cylinder with a small outlet in the base and mounted in an oil bath. Oil is heated to a specified temperature and the time taken for a measured amount to run through the hole is recorded.

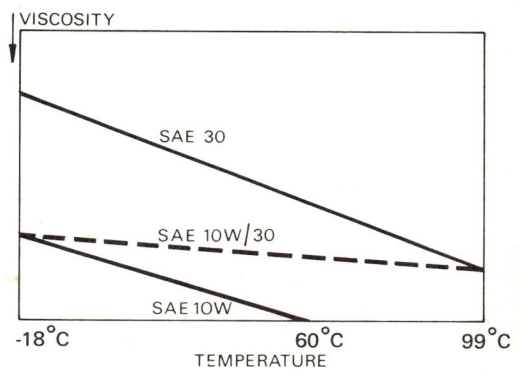

The continuous lines on the graph show the viscosity of SAE 10 W oil at 60 deg. C and a heavier SAE 30 oil at 99 deg. C. The broken line shows how the thinning process is slowed down when a VI improver is added thus making a multigrade oil SAE 10 W/30.

Oils are mainly sold by a viscosity range or specification. The most commonly used specifications are those laid down by the American Society of Automobile Engineers (hence the A.S.A.E. numbers). The Americans still do not use metric units widely and the A.S.A.E. tests are not carried out in metric units. If and when the Americans do metricate, the specifications will remain the same, only the laboratory tests will change. We will still use, for example, a 20–50W oil for a typical engine oil or an E.P.90 as a typical gear oil.

## LUBRICANT STORE

Get round the problem of keeping tractor lubrication equipment, oil and grease in one place and available when needed by making a simple rack with a few lengths of angle iron and pieces of plywood.

Brackets made of sheet steel and bolted to the plywood back hold the grease-guns and oil-cans. Store lubricants in their containers on the floor by the rack.

A further refinement shown in the photograph is a built-in drip tray below the welded mesh to prevent oil staining the floor.

# TRACTORS: ENGINE GOVERNORS

An engine governor maintains a constant speed under varying loads and protects the engine and ancillary equipment against high speeds when the load is reduced.

By controlling the supply of fuel to the engine it controls the speed, which is important when driving pto tackle requiring an exact speed.

There are three basic types of governor: centrifugal (sometimes called mechanical), pneumatic and hydraulic.

The centrifugal is the type most commonly used in agricultural diesel engines.

Two or more weights 'A' are pivoted on a carrier or spindle 'B', which is driven at the same speed as the engine camshaft through the timing gears. When the engine is running the weights, which are hinged at one end, are free to fly outwards or inwards, according to the speed at which they are driven. Their position is also controlled by a spring 'C'.

As the engine speed increases or decreases, the weights move in and out and this movement is transmitted to the fuel valve 'E' by a push-rod 'D' which, in turn, controls the amount of fuel delivered to the injectors.

The hydraulic governor is less widely used but it is just as efficient. It utilises the action of a spring against the working pressure of the fuel generated by a feed pump, inside the injector pump, this pressure varying with engine speed.

A shuttle valve, with spring pressure acting on one side and fuel pressure on the other, is connected to the fuel delivery valve. As the engine speed increases so does the fuel pressure and the shuttle valve is pushed against the spring to reduce fuel delivery. When the engine speed decreases the reverse action takes place and the fuel delivery is increased.

Faulty governors cause lack of power, poor engine response to increased load and 'racing' when the load is decreased.

Most governor trouble can be traced to lack of lubrication, worn or loose parts or weakened springs. If the bearing surfaces become dry and gummy, the governor will be slow to respond to speed changes and if parts are excessively worn it may jam open or become spasmodic in operation. 'Hunting' is the term given to governor action when it produces a fast-slow-fast-slow effect and this is usually most noticeable at slow engine speeds, when a small throttle movement makes a big difference.

The adjustments are factory set and sealed and should not be tampered with. Some drivers 'open up' the governor and say the tractor performs better. This is a fallacy and does more harm than good. Low idle setting is the only adjustment necessary. For other problems call your dealer.

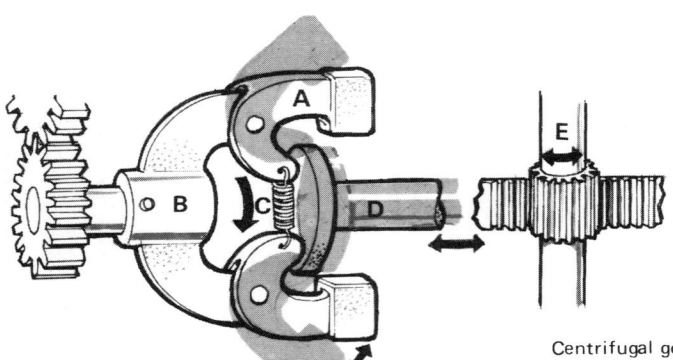

Centrifugal governor: On many modern tractors speeds are varied from about 600 to 2,220 rpm.

# TRACTORS: TAPPET ADJUSTMENT

Moderr tractors are so complex that when major components like the hydraulics go wrong, a dealer's mechanic has to be called in. But there are many servicing jobs that can be done by the driver. One of these is tappet adjustment.

A valve in an engine is opened and closed by the cam shaft through a push rod which operates a centrally-pivoted rocker arm. As one end of the rocker arm is raised by the push rod, the other end presses down on the valve stem and opens the valve.

Since different metals expand at different rates, there must be a gap between the valve stem and rocker arm to allow the valve to seat properly when hot.

This gap is referred to as valve or tappet clearance. If the clearance is too small there will be excessive wear on the end of the valve stem and burning of the valve seat.

Too big a gap will mean a noisy engine, and valves will fail to open properly. Wrong setting either way results in poor engine performance.

First step in adjustment is to rotate the crankshaft until the piston in the cylinder on which the valves are to be adjusted is at top dead centre with both valves closed. You can then measure valve clearances with a feeler gauge and adjust them accordingly.

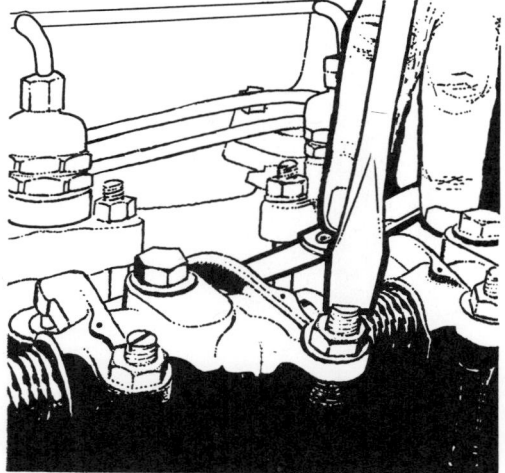

Slide the feeler gauge between the valve stem and rocker arm. Tighten the screw until the feeler is a light dragging fit. Then tighten up the nut while still holding the screw firm.

This method can prove difficult for someone not familiar with engines, and many mechanics prefer the following way.

For a four-cylinder engine, which has two valves to each cylinder and so has eight tappets to adjust, take the number 9 as a guide. Work from the front, and turn over the engine by the fan until valve 8 is fully open. Then you can adjust the gap on tappet 1 (8+1=9).

Similarly, to adjust tappet 2, valve 7 must be fully open (2+7=9). Continue like this until all gaps are correct.

Use the number 13 as a guide if you are working on a six-cylinder engine.

Three-cylinder engines have a different type of cam-shaft, and the maker's handbook will tell you the adjustment order.

Finally, contrary to popular belief, it is not necessary to do the adjustments with the engine hot.

# SERVICING TRACTOR DYNAMOS

Dynamos on tractors rarely give trouble. If they do break down a service exchange unit costs only a few pounds.

The main problem is brush wear. Brushes are easily replaced—a new pair costs a few pence—if caught in time, and it is worthwhile inspecting them every few months to check for wear. Look through the holes in the back plate of the dynamo and if the brushes are less than 5 or 6 mm long they need renewing. Otherwise they will wear until the wire connected to the brushes comes into contact with the armature and wears a deep groove in the copper segments of the commutator as it revolves.

First step in dismantling a dynamo is to remove the two long retaining screws in the back-plate. Lift the back-plate, complete with brushes and springs, gently off the main dynamo body.

Undo the screws holding the brush wire and remove the brushes from their guides. Lift the springs off their locating pins and wash the back-plate in petrol to remove dirt and grease.

While the back-plate dries remove the main dynamo case and inspect the commutator. If there is a ridge more than 1.5 mm deep where the brushes have been in contact with it the commutator will need skimming down on a lathe—a job for the dealer. Light rubbing with glass-paper will

Remove the end-plate, with brushes, first.

usually remove any carbon smear and small surface pits and dents.

After cleaning up the commutator the mica insulation must be undercut and removed below the level of the commutator surface. Do this with a thin knife blade or small hacksaw blade, pulling the blade away from the armature. Blow off with an air-line to remove loose particles, which should be wiped clean from the rest of the dynamo.

Reassemble and fit new brushes, making sure they slide freely in their guides and the screws are tight. If the springs are broken replace them. Fit the end-plate, pushing the brushes over the commutator with a small screwdriver and taking

care not to chip the brittle carbon. Ensure the endplate dowel is properly located in its recess. Make sure the brush wires do not get trapped between the end-plate and main body of the dynamo. Tighten the two end screws and re-fit the dynamo to the tractor. The whole job will take about an hour and will make a dynamo fit for many more hours of service.

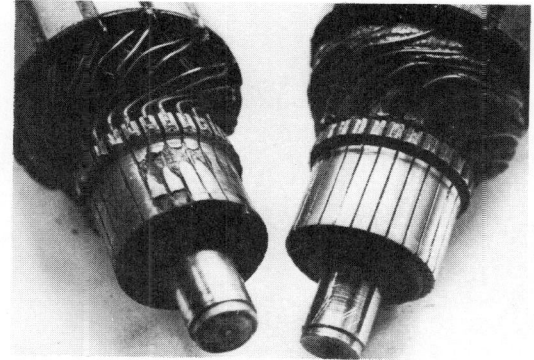

A new dynamo is the only answer in this case.

Make sure the brushes slide easily in the guides.

Rest the armature on a vice while undercutting the copper segments. Remove only around 0.1 to 0.2 mm of insulation.

Gently prise brushes over the commutator to refit.

# OVERHAULS: THE PLOUGH

### CHECKING ALIGNMENT OF BEAMS AND FRAMES

A poorly adjusted or incorrectly mounted plough results in bad work and wasted tractor power. Fuel consumption per hectare increases, the cost of replacing wearing parts goes up and work output drops.

A good commercial job of ploughing combines speed with quality of work leaving uniform furrows with a clean lever surface free from weed and trash. There must also be plenty of soil available for discs and harrows to get to grips with during subsequent cultivations. For this the plough, like all implements, needs proper maintance.

Take advantage of a wet spell to do a complete overhaul.

Equipped with an average tool kit plus a straight edge ruler and a plumb line, it can be done in a day. To make things easier and save barked knuckles, give all nuts and bolts a liberal dose of penetrating oil a couple of days before.

### Diagnosis

All measurements should be taken with the tractor and plough standing on a level surface and to obtain greater accuracy it is wise to fit a new set of shares.

Field setting problems which arise from bent or twisted beams or main frame members may show up in work as uneven furrows, varying depth of work, or, probably the worst fault of all—crabbing sideways.

First carry out checks for distorted main-frame members and beams. Distortion is chiefly vertical or lateral. Vertical distortion is checked by measuring from under the share point to the under edge of the beam. The distance should be the same for all bodies. Small discrepancies can sometimes be corrected by individual pitch adjusters if fitted; otherwise the share or the body must be shimmed.

Use a spirit level and a straight edge to detect main frame distortions. A steel bar clamped across the frame while the bolts are slack may pull a twisted plough back into shape.

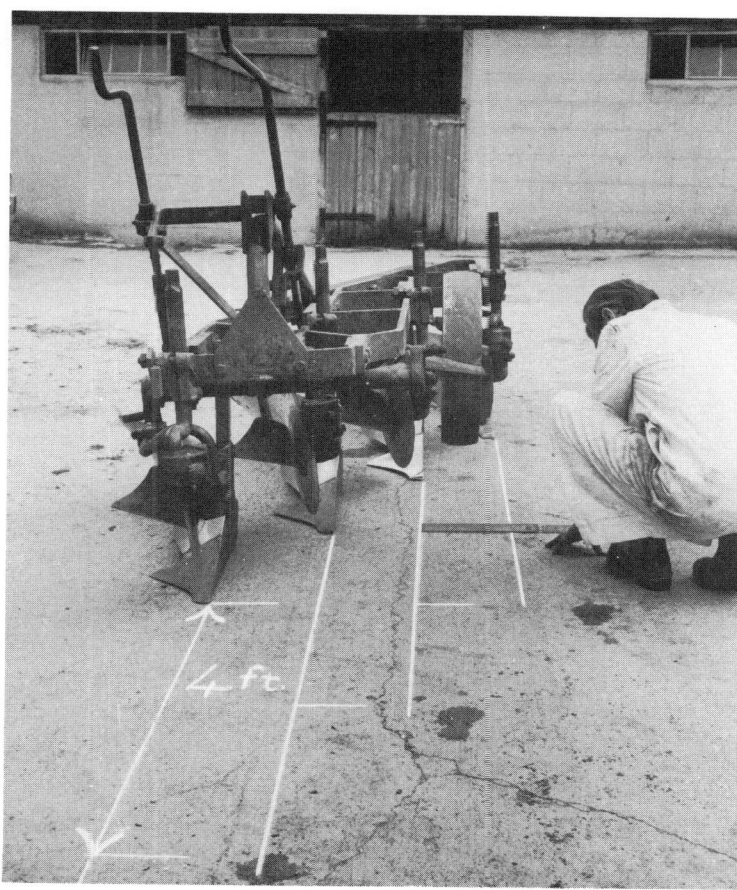

## BEAM DISTORTION

When a beam is distorted laterally the share will be taking too much land or not enough. It is not always possible to detect by eye a bent beam; discrepancies will become obvious if one of the three following methods is used.

1. Place a straight edge along the landside and share point of each body in turn and draw extended lines for a distance of at least 1 metre remembering to allow for the longer rear landside. The distance between the extended lines should be the same for all bodies.

2. Place a straight edge along the share points.

3. Drop a plumb line down the face of the beam directly above the share point and mark the place where it contacts the share. The marks should all be in the same position in relation to the edge of the share.

Having got the main frame right, check on body alignment, discoulter and skim settings. Making sure, too, that the hitch, draught line and tractor wheel settings are right. These operations are described on the next page.

Checking the position of the bodies relative to each other may be done by extending the line of each landside forward on a level surface. These lines should be parallel and an equal distance apart. A discrepancy of more than about 10 mm in 1m (½in in 4ft) indicates a bent or twisted beam.

An easier way of checking the relative position of bodies—but not as accurate as the extended line method—is to place a straight edge along the share points.

## HITCHING, DRAUGHT AND WHEEL SETTING

The plough must be hitched up correctly to make a workable unit. If the top link is in line with the centre line of the tractor the draught line is correct. Crabbing increases drawbar pull and every extra 90 kg demands an additional one kilowatt.

The power needed to pull a plough is calculated by the following formula: the furrow width in metres x depth of furrow in metres x number of furrows x soil resistance.

For example, a 4 furrow plough with 350 mm bodies working 250 mm deep in medium to heavy loam would require a drawbar pull of: 0.350 m x 0.250 m x 4 x 70,000 N/m$^2$ = 24,500 newtons drawbar pull. Remember that tractor power is measured in kilowatts and 1 watt = 1 Nm/s (see page 44). So if you know the speed of ploughing, you can calculate the drawbar power in kW required to pull the plough. For example, if the plough discussed above were to be pulled at 10 kmph it would require

$$24{,}500 \times \frac{10 \times 1{,}000}{60 \times 60} \text{ watts} = 68 \text{ kW.}$$

drawbar     speed in
pull          metres per second

Soil resistance varies from 35,000 N/m$^2$ in light sandy soils to 100,500 N/m$^2$ in heavy clay. An average of 70,000 N/m$^2$ would apply to medium to heavy loam. Always take the farm's heaviest soil in making calculations.

When ploughing the top link and plough frame should be in line with the tractor.

If rear wheel setting is wrong there will be difficulty in getting the correct front furrow width. This may be obtained by changing the position of the cross shaft in relation to the main frame or by turning the crossshaft adjusting lever. But this does not ensure a true draught line. So before coupling the plough to the tractor see that the rear wheel centres are correct according to tyre size and front furrow width. On 12.4—36 (11 x 36) tyres the tractor rear wheels need to be at 1,320 mm centres for 250 mm wide furrows, 1,420 mm centres for 300 mm furrows and 1,520 mm centres for 350 mm furrows. On 16.9—30 (14 x 30) tyres, 1,420 mm centres are needed for 250 mm furrows, 1,520 mm centres for 300 mm furrows and 1,625 mm centres for 350 mm furrows.

Altering rear wheel centres may necessitate moving the front ones. The inside of the front tyres should be in line with the inside of the rear for ploughing.

For coupling on uneven ground first attach the left-hand link, then the right-hand one, using the linkage levelling and cross-shaft adjusters to line up the pin, and finally the top link. Check chains should be slack when the plough is in work and tight enough to prevent the plough from swinging and fouling the tractor tyres when it is lifted.

### IN-THE-FIELD PLOUGH CHECK

Having checked over the plough in the workshop and attached it to the tractor, we must do the remaining settings in the field.

To get well-matched bouts from both sets of bodies, various adjustments, including carefully setting levels across and along the plough's axis and front furrow width, are essential. Failure to adjust level settings properly will give a different depth of ploughing on one set of bodies. A small front furrow width means it will take longer than necessary to plough the field, and give an uneven-looking finish to the furrows. Wide front furrows will increase draught, and if too wide the furrow will stand on its side and not bury the surface rubbish. A depth to width ratio of 1:1½ is a good average.

Plough manufacturers have various ways of altering furrow width and tilt, so the handbook should be consulted at all times.

Top link setting will affect lengthways levelling of the plough. Too short a top link gives a deep front furrow with the last one much shallower and broken furrow wall (1) and the converse for too long a setting on the top link. Check for even depth of furrows with a tape measure just behind the mouldboards (2). Another way is to squat a few metres away from the plough's side and by eye check that the beam is the same height above ground at both the front and rear furrows. A correctly-set top link will allow the rear landside to just press on the bottom of furrow and keep a clean furrow bottom (see next page, 3).

Headlands should be carefully marked out in order to leave sufficient space for the plough to be lifted out of work on the move. Many ploughmen stop when the front wheels touch the hedge and lift the plough out of solid ground, overloading the hydraulics on the tractor. Remember also when ploughing out the headlands to use both sets of bodies equally, otherwise one will wear more than the other. Skim and disc coulter settings are as for conventional ploughs (see page 79).

**1**

**2**

3

One final point, if the plough is to be left idle for any length of time—paint the shiny parts with **fresh oil** to prevent rust and subsequent scouring problems when ploughing starts again.

## BODY ALIGNMENT

Plough bodies can be divided into three categories—general purpose, semi-digger and digger. Each needs a different depth setting in relation to furrow width. General purpose bodies work best at a furrow depth to width ratio of $1:1\frac{1}{2}$; for example, **200 mm** deep and **300 mm** wide. Semi-digger types work deeper in relation to width, **250 mm** for **300 mm** and digger types generally need a **1:1** ratio or square furrow. The illustrations show common faults and how to correct them.

The nose of a body sometimes becomes bent; to detect this, place a straight edge along the underside of the share and landslide. The gap at (A), known as the suck, should be the same for each body. Metal packing strips for pegged-on shares or a flattened cigarette packet for bolt-on shares can often be used to correct matters.

The rear mouldboard on this plough is 20 mm too low. They should all be the same height and the distance between each one equal. This is more difficult to correct and to spot when buying second-hand.

On ploughs with adjustable mouldboards care must be taken not to push them out too far, because this will increase the draught load and may cause the furrows to roll back, especially when ploughing grassland.

Moving the mouldboards in or out also alters the width of the furrow trench. It is an adjustment which comes in handy when using a tractor with oversized tyres to prevent the last furrow from being squashed.

Setting up the reversible plough is often looked upon as being much easier than the conventional types, but this is not necessarily true. Although the settings suggested for conventional ploughs apply equally to reversibles, there are a few extra points to watch. It is essential that both tractor tyres are at equal pressure and lift links must be exactly the same length. This is to ensure even depth front furrows in both directions, and the main frame must be parallel to the ground at all times to achieve level work. Conventional ploughs may be tilted in certain conditions to help turn the furrows.

The measurement at (A) should be set the same for all bodies during the overhaul. Small corrections can be made later in the field.

1

## PREPARING A REVERSIBLE PLOUGH

In order to get well matched ploughing in both directions from a reversible plough, all measurements and settings on the left-hand set of bodies must be the same as those on the right-hand bodies.

Working on a level surface, carry out the following checks.

If pitch varies from share to share, uneven

work is inevitable. Fit a new set of shares, then as a rough check, place the straight edge along the line of the shares to see it touches all of them. A more accurate method is to measure vertically from the share point to the underside of the beam (1). To adjust, place shims under the share. On some ploughs pitch can be altered by an eccentric bolt.

If mouldboards are not the same distance apart all along their length, uneven width furrows will result. If they are too wide, draught will be excessive and the furrow will roll back. Check them by measuring the distance between share points and then the distance between the backs of the mouldboards.

The mouldboards can be adjusted by the tie rod behind each furrow, or again, by shims. Final setting can be done in the field.

Lateral distortion of the legs can be measured by placing the straight edge at right angles to the main frame near the share points, and using the tape to check that the offset between point and straight edge is the same on both sets of bodies.

The rear landsides must be parallel and in line with each other. Swing the plough on its side, place the straight edge across the main beam and at right angles to it, and check that both landsides are an equal distance from the straight edge (2).

If the turnover mechanism is hydraulically

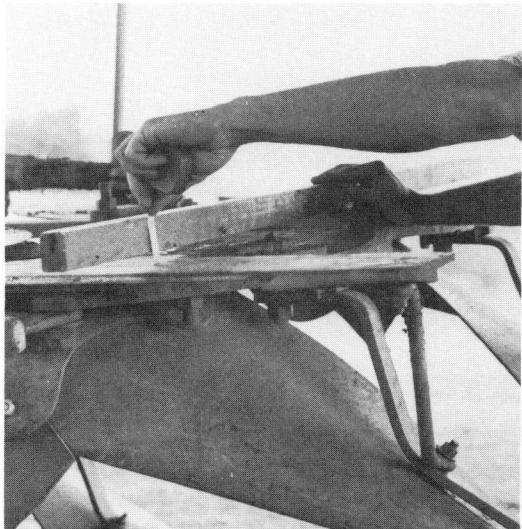

2

3

operated, check the couplings and hoses for leaks, cracks or perishing. If it is mechanical, then chances are it will have worn with use and the plough will turn over with a bang. This may distort the plough, so adjust the linkage to give a nice easy turnover.

Before attaching the tractor to the plough, check front and rear wheel settings in the maker's handbook. Failure to to this will cause the tractor to crab, resulting in an incorrectly sized front furrow, and will place

extra strain on both tractor and plough. In heavy conditions it may be necessary to add weights and water ballast to the rear wheels. Make sure each wheel is equally ballasted. On hilly land, or when lifting out of work, weights must be fitted to the front of the tractor, because a reversible plough is so heavy that the front wheels will lift off the ground. The tractor could overturn.

Also, the lift rods must be the same length or else the plough will tilt (3)

## HARD-SURFACING PLOUGHSHARES

The rate of wear on the cutting edges and points of a ploughshare can be slowed down by hard-surfacing them. This way share life can be doubled.

Tools required are an oxy-acetylene gas welder, a portable grinder or file, rods that deposit abrasion-resistant metals and a basic knowledge of gas welding (see pages 108—112). Hard-surfacing the new share shown here took one rod. A partially-worn share is more expensive to do, requiring more rods and time to build it up to its original level. Also, soil will have been driven into the metal, making it difficult to clean. Impurities will float to the surface of the weld pool, interfering with the fusion process and giving a poor weld.

First, areas to be treated should be cleaned down to the bare metal.

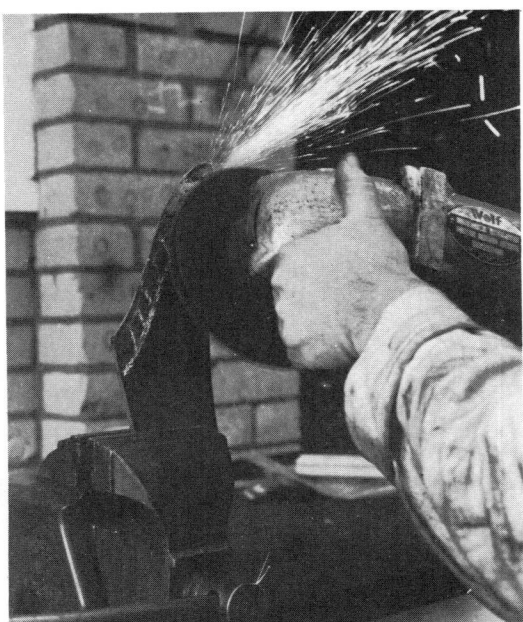

(3) The new share should be cleaned down to the bare metal.

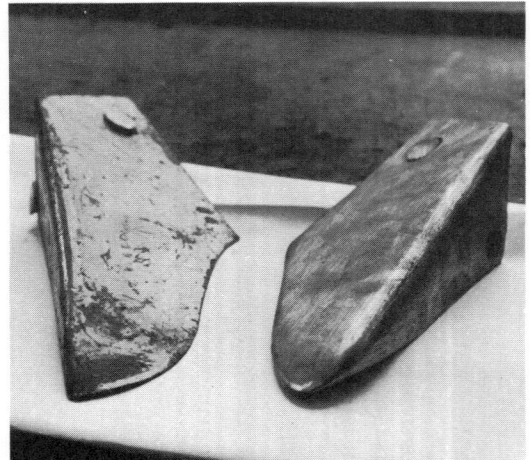

(1) A new share (left) takes less time to hard-surface and requires less deposit.

(2) Areas to be treated are shown by the chalk-marks.

The rod used in the job illustrated was a wear-resistant alloy steel that deposited small amounts of carbon, silicon, manganese and other metals in the weld.

Ordinary rods will not do, as they are generally intended to give a soft deposit that is strong and ductile. Alloys that resist abrasion have higher degrees of hardness and are prone to crack under impact. Check with your supplier that the rod will do the job.

A No 10 nozzle was used with pressures of 0.25 bar on both oxygen and acetylene bottles. Flame length is about two-and-a-half times the ordinary neutral cone length. This will help deposit more carbon in the weld.

Hold the rod and torch at an angle of about 25 deg to the work. Pre-heat a small area of share and as soon as the metal starts to 'sweat' and bubbles begin to appear on the surface dip the rod into the sweat pool and melt the rod on to the share. Take care not to get the parent metal of the share too molten or there will be too much mixing of the rod deposit and the parent metal, giving a softer deposit.

Make a bead about 12 mm wide on the top surface of the share, using a weaving, up and down motion with the rod. Underneath the share point hard-surface an area from the point to 25 mm farther back. Lay a narrow bead along the land side or 'suck' edge.

(4) Laying a bead along the front cutting edge.

Finally leave to cool and wire-brush off any scale or slag.

Much cheaper ways of hard-facing have now been developed and these involve less skill. Usually they do not create such thick layers of deposit but are otherwise just as satisfactory. Spray welding with a special torch or hard-facing with a paste and conventional torch are useful techniques for the farm workshop. The equipment and techniques are described on page 122.

Discs must be renewed when they get into this state.

## HOT RIVETING A DISC COULTER

To renew disc coulters first place the disc in a vice and grind or chisel off the rivet heads. Do this from the disc end of the rivet, not from the casting end, otherwise you may crack the casting with the chisel or bite into it with the grinder.

Carefully punch out the old rivets and clean off dirt on the flange to ensure proper seating of the new disc.

Remove rivet heads from the disc side to avoid damaging the casting.

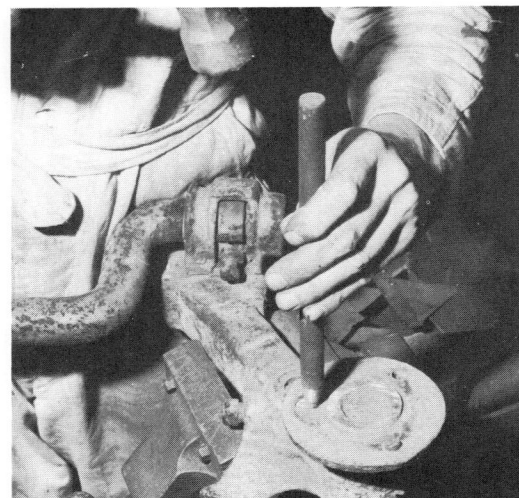

Punch out the rivets through the back of the casting. Take care . . . a mis-hit may crack the casting.

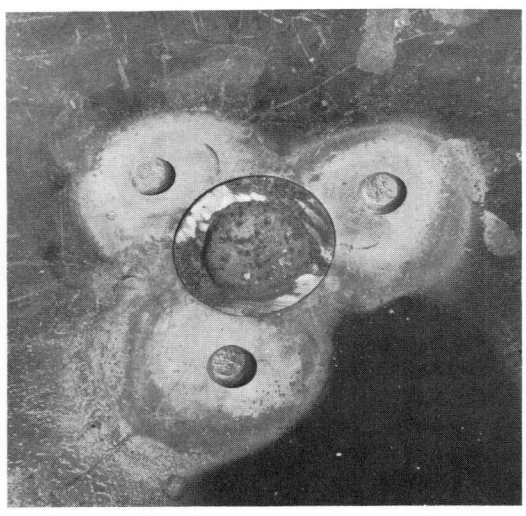

The finished job—a tight joint with three nicely rounded rivet heads.

Use the gas welding torch to bring the rivet to forging heat, then push the rivet through the casting, place the head on a solid surface—a blacksmith's anvil is ideal—put the disc over the rivet and seat it on the casting flange.

While an assistant holds the disc to keep the rivet head on the anvil, tap the rivet with a hammer to spread it in the hole. Use a snap to form the head. Repeat process with the other two rivets.

## DISC COULTERS AND SKIMS

The initial setting for disc coulters is usually 20 mm or one finger width from the edge of the shares to the discs and cutting just deep enough to leave a clean furrow wall.

Discs set too deep may prevent the plough penetrating and cause excessive wear in the bearings. Coulter stops should be set to give equal swing on either side of the share. Normal fore and aft setting is with the centre of the discs slightly behind the point to help penetration. Discs should never be angled to land as this puts a tremendous strain on the bearing; angling should be towards the ploughing, making sure they are all equal.

Skim coulter setting for average conditions is just deep enough to ensure that all weeds and trash are buried. Set the point of the skimmers as close to the discs as possible without actually touching them and the heels slightly farther away.

If they are set too deep or at the wrong angle, the skimmings do not go into the furrow bottom, causing hollows under the furrows, and there is a danger that they will be dragged on to the top during subsequent cultivations.

The plough is now ready to take to the field. Next it must be hitched to the tractor correctly and the whole outfit lined up.

With skims at front of the discs, there is less chance of trash build-up at the back of the skim and skimmings are cut before the furrows become loose.

Dismantle coulter bearings and wash off old grease. Pack with clean grease and re-adjust until they just spin freely.

Final disc adjustment can only be done in the field. To make this easier, set them all to the same measurements during the overhaul. 'A' 50 mm, 'B' 15 to 20 mm, 'C' centre of disc just behind the share point.

# OVERHAULS: THE BEET HARVESTER

## WEB CHAINS, ROLLERS AND COUPLINGS

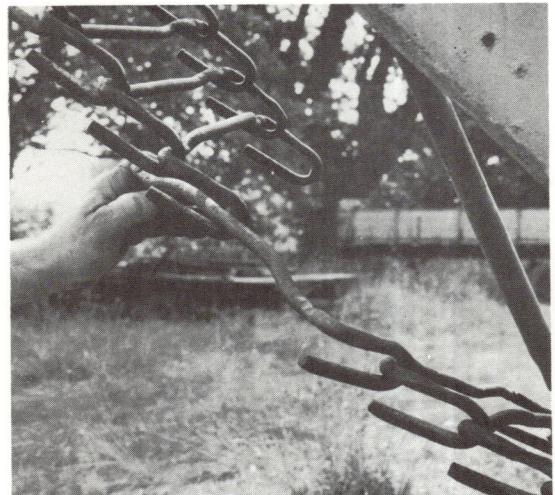

Checking a web chain the easy way: first attach one link to the two loose ends of the chain and, using it as a lever, pull the two sections together.

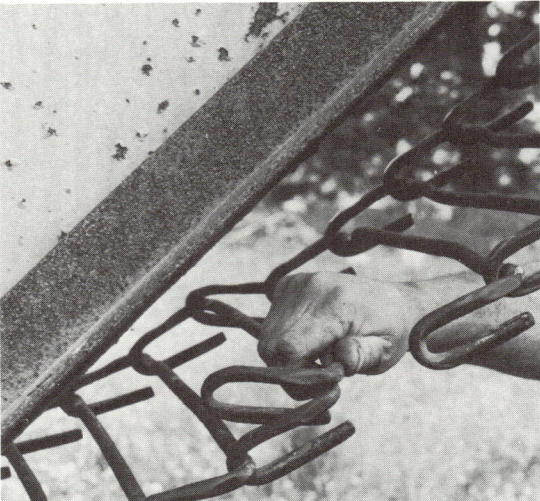

Next, hook the link on to the lower section. Pull links as close as possible by gripping with both hands and connect.

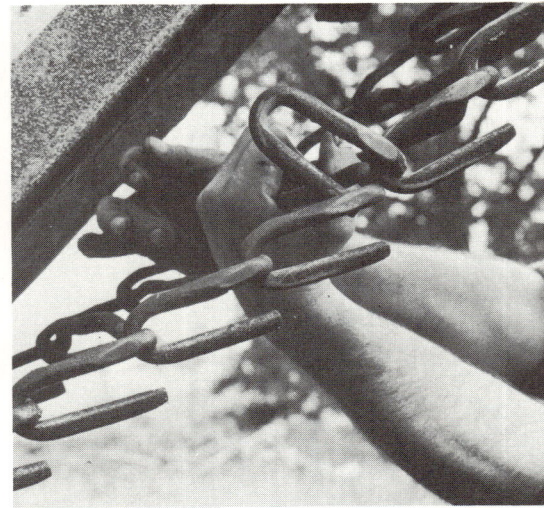

Final hooking up is thus confined to one end. Even with a new, tight chain, one hammer blow should complete the joint.

Preparing a beet harvester for its season's lifting is not as involved as preparing more complicated machines such as combines and balers. Nevertheless, a few hours spent on checking, adjusting and greasing will pay dividends when the going gets tough. There are few machines that have a tougher life.

First overhaul the web chains. Check each individual link for wear at the point where it comes in contact with its counterpart and replace any that are severely worn. Links worn more than half their diameter will probably fracture during work and it is far easier to change them in the workshop than in the field when tne chain is covered in muck.

Repairing links by welding is not really practicable. Welded links tend to break off either side of the weld, but if in an emergency a weld has to be made ensure that both ends of the link are the same diameter after welding. If they are not, the chain will run out of line or snag on the drive sprocket.

Sprockets often become hooked causing the chain to hang on or jump off. Some sprockets may be reversed, but this should only be attempted if they have not been allowed to become

An example of a badly worn and hooked sprocket. The profile of the teeth has been changed by the amount of wear shown at A. This will cause excessive strain in bearings, shafts and chains.

more than half worn.

Adjustment of sag for a web chain will depend on whether it is running horizontally or at an angle; normally it should be just tight enough to allow easy joining. If the going is sticky, a slightly slacker chain will give a better cleaning action.

Chain idler guide rollers should be free running. Check that they have not worn on one side only. Most manufacturers mount these guide rollers on chilled cast bearings which have glass hard bearing surfaces. These should not be

greased or oiled as they are not sealed to keep out dust and dirt. Grease and soil when mixed together, make an excellent grinding paste.

Sliding couplings on pto and other drive shafts tend to seize or become sticky during winter storage. To prevent damaging the universal joints through excessive end thrust clean off all the old stiff grease by washing in paraffin and smear with fresh grease. When pumping grease into the joints, care must be taken to avoid blowing out the dust seals; one or two pumps are usually sufficient.

These two roller chains are completely ruined through lack of attention. The majority of the link-pins are seized solid and rollers are caked in soil and rust. They should have been removed and left to soak in an oil bath.

Worn guide rollers, if not attended to, will increase the rate of wear in the web chain links. Remember these types of bushes must not be greased or oiled.

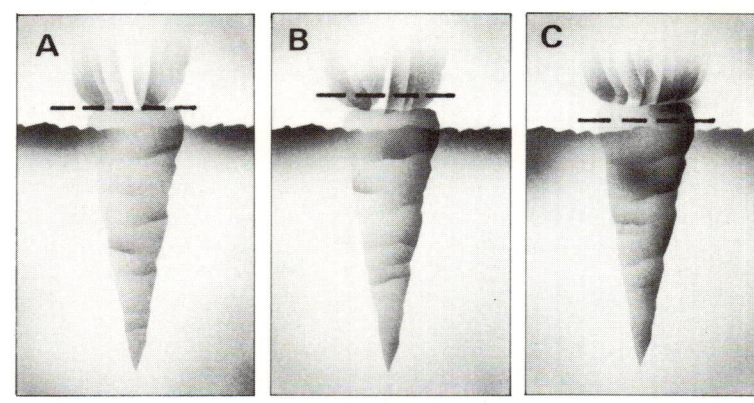

A—correct;  B—under topping;  C—over topping.

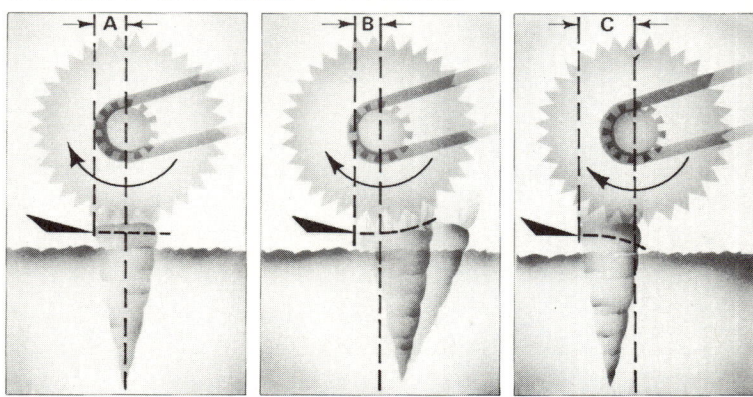

A squirt of release oil on all bolts and set screws used for adjusting will save time and knuckle damage in the field.

The slip clutch should be dismantled, inspected for wear, cleaned and reassembled dry. On no account put oil or grease on the friction surfaces and do not overtighten.

A—correct; feeler wheel grips the beet all the time during cutting. B—cutting too early; knife cutting before the feeler wheel grips the beet. C—cutting too late; feeler wheel running off the crown before the cut is completed.

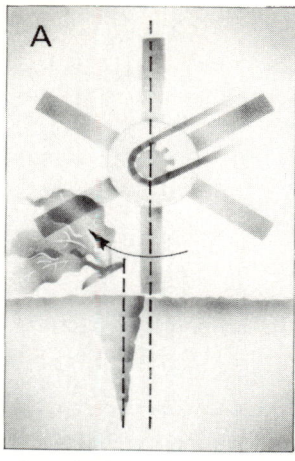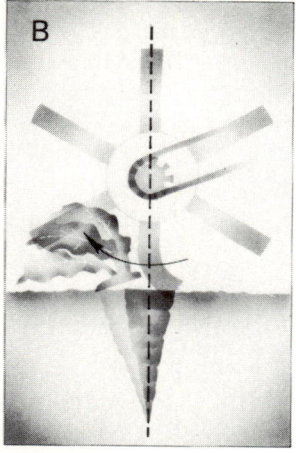

(Top A) Correct setting; flails slightly offset and just brushing the ground. (Bottom B) Incorrect setting; flails set directly over the beet will not throw the tops the required distance. If too close to the ground beet will be dislodged and also cause damage to the flails.

## TOPPING UNITS AND FLAILS

The setting of the beet harvester's topping unit will to a great extent determine how much beet is lost or wasted. As a guide keep the knife flat in all directions, have the feeler wheel centred on the crown of the beet and remember that the amount of crown to be removed is governed by the distance between knife and feeler wheel. If tops are long and sturdy this distance needs to be greater than for small, drooping tops.

A return of 'no top tare' means that too much crown has been removed.

Efficiency of the topping unit governs lifting rate of a harvester. Check that serrations on the feeler wheel are sharp, the assembly free to float, the knife sharp, and the knife breakaway device working.

Rubber flails take a pounding during a season's lifting, especially in stony conditions. Check flails for fractures where they bolt to the hub and replace any that are suspect. It is often wise to replace the complete set of flails to ensure the spinner is balanced. At the same time, take a look at the drive chain and sprocket—shock loads transmitted by flails hitting stones tend to stretch the links and wear the sprocket teeth.

Flails can do more harm than good if not set in the correct position. For normal setting they work best just touching the ground, but on light, sandy soil they need to be slightly higher, to prevent beet being knocked out of line and missed on the next round.

Adjust the trash disc to cut off enough of the beet top to allow the knife arm a clear run. Failure to do this will result in trash build-up on the arm and blockages.

To overcome crabbing on sliding ground, move the trash disc into the centre of the two so that it cuts a furrow deep enough to guide the harvester wheel. Although this will cause a build-up of trash around the topping unit and knife arm, it is probably the lesser of the two evils.

## SHARE WIDTH SETTING

Having got the topping part right, turn to the lifting mechanism.

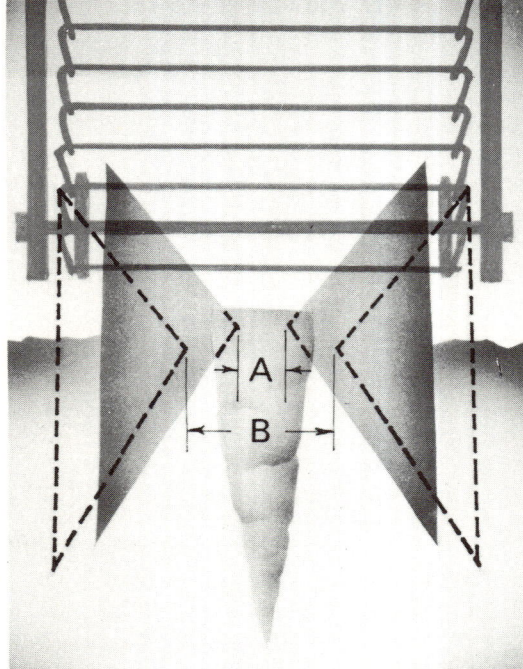

Share width setting is governed by the size of the beet; the average setting is about 40 mm. A is correct for the beet shown in the diagram, but B is wide and would leave a lot of beet in the ground.

For machines with lifter wheels instead of shares it may be necessary to reset the tapered roller bearings. First remove the grease cap and the cotter pin from the castellated retaining nut, tighten the nut until the wheel is stiff to turn, back off the nut one flat or until a slot lines up with the hole in the axle and re-fit the cotter pin. Fill the grease cap with the recommended grease before reassembling.

Lifter wheels, like shares, don't last for ever. When it becomes necessary to change them don't throw away the old set; they may come in handy in an emergency. Worn wheels do not block up as quickly as new ones and some contractors carry a set to get out of trouble in heavy and sticky conditions.

Lifting shares, if caught before they have worn too far, may be built up with weld. The lift of a share can be greatly increased by welding a piece of spring steel on to the heel, taking care to re-tain the original profile.

When working hard ground new shares often break off at the point. Fitting a worn set may overcome the problem. The average share width setting is 40 mm, usually obtained by adding or re-moving shims. Mounting bolts must be really tight to prevent the shares moving when in work.

How much soil should be lifted with the beet? This is a case of setting to suit conditions, but at all times the beet should be lifted with tap-roots intact.

In light soil it is advisable to take a little more soil than usual to safeguard against losing the smaller beet, but remember that the factory will reject any load that has an excessive amount of soil.

## FIELD OPERATION

Some harvesters are fitted with an attachment for opening out a field, but too often this back-breaking job has to be done by hand. Sharp shovels and dutch hoes are the best tools for this job.

After the field or fields have been prepared for the machine, it is good practice to do all the machine opening at one go. This saves having to readjust wheel widths each time on entering a new field. Open out during the most favourable ground and weather conditions; it saves beet and simplifies what is sometimes a difficult operation.

The correct wheel setting for tractor and harvester is important and it is best to have it right from the outset. Tractor wheel centres should be three times the row width; for example, the setting for 500 mm rows would be 1,500 mm centres.

The harvester wheels during opening out have to be centred between the rows, but for normal operation the right-hand wheel—looking from the rear of machine—should be centred between the rows and following tractor wheel, whereas the left-hand wheel should run in the bottom of the furrow made by lifting the previous row. This helps to keep the harvester stable and follow the drills, especially on sidling ground.

Moving the hitching position of the machine on the linkage drawbar instead of adjusting the wheels will result in either the harvester or the tractor crabbing. This can cause damage to the beet through the wheels hitting them or, even more troublesome, disturb the firm soil at the base of the beet and make it difficult for the topping unit to work efficiently.

Carry a selection of spare parts. A first-aid kit comprising a few web chain links, roller chain links and half links, a couple of lifting shares, a set of rubber flails and two sharp knives will help in an emergency.

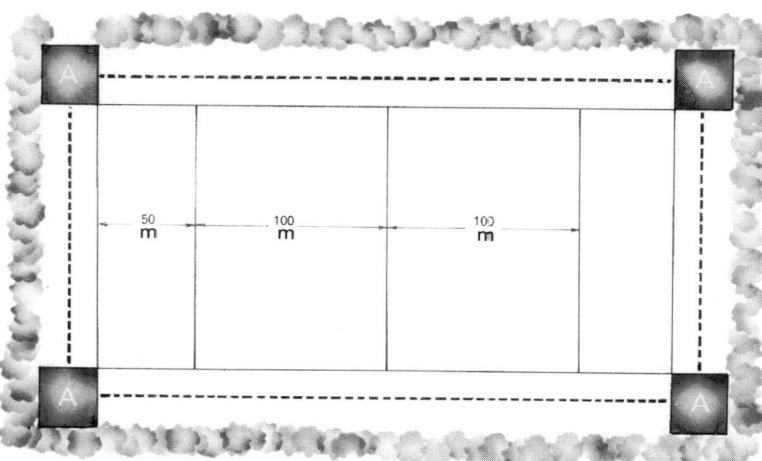

50 m  100 m  100 m

(Left) Opening out. Lift "A" by hand. Take harvester down the middle row of headland and lift beet towards the hedge. This, usually the wettest part of the field, should be lifted first. Then drive back lifting towards the centre of the field to remove rest of the headland.
Divide remainder into lands (50m is normal). Over-large lands will increase out-of-work running on headlands.

Adjusting feeder flails to strike the edges of lifter wheels minimises soil build-up.

# OVERHAULS: THE MANURE SPREADER

The manure spreader, above all other farm tackle, works under severe conditions and requires extra care.

A high pressure water hose, grease-gun and oil-can rank as the spreader's best friends. Regular hosing flushes off the ammonia and corrosive salts in the muck and prevents them attacking the metal and paintwork.

Worn and broken parts can then be spotted before they cause a major failure, grease nipples are in sight and overhauls are easier.

When doing an overhaul take each section and drive of the machine and follow it right through. The best point to start is on the drive mechanism.

Ground driven machines have many more working parts and require more attention.

First check the pawl and ratchet drives in both wheels. Remove each wheel in turn and wash off the old grease and dirt. Inspect for wear, especially the pawls and springs. Leading corners of the pawls become rounded and should be renewed or built up with weld. Weakened springs may be temporarily strengthened by fitting small washers or spacing pieces in their locating holes, but take care not to make them coil-bound.

One wheel hub will carry the main drive sprocket. The chain must drop centrally on to the sprocket and be fully engaged when the lever is in the drive position. The sprocket has to withstand the full strain of all the driving force re-

If wheel end float is more than 2 mm the contact area of the drive pawls is reduced.

A broken pawl spring (see A) will reduce the effectiveness of each feeding stroke. The split pin securing the ratchet wheel (see B) is incorrectly fitted.

This is the kind of fault that shows up once the muck has been washed off.

quired and if the chain is incorrectly adjusted it will jump over the teeth.

The opposite wheel operates the conveyor chain feed mechanism, usually consisting of a cam with three or four lobes, a ratchet wheel and actuating lever. Check on the amount of wear in ratchet pawls, condition of the springs, lever pin wear and the efficiency of the linkage return springs.

Ensure the tyres are correctly fitted. The point of the 'V' tread bars should be trailing in direction of rotation—pointing to the rear of the spreader. Correct air pressure is important to the performance of ground driven machines. They rely on the grip obtained by the tyre for all the drives and a too low pressure will result in poor spreading and tyre wall damage as well as increased draught.

The wheels should have no more than 2 mm end float to ensure the correct engagement of the pawls inside the hubs. Special stepped collars are usually fitted to enable any excessive free play to be taken up. If there is no adjustment left on the collars, a washer fitted between the collar and the hub will do the job.

## DRIVE SHAFTS

On power driven machines, where the main drive shaft runs under the body, it is worthwhile to check that the shaft has not been damaged by driving over rough tracks or through rutted gateways.

Some pto models have square section drive shafts and these can be coupled up incorrectly. If the universal joints are not in line, as shown (below), jerky drive will result and play havoc with the needle roller bearings.

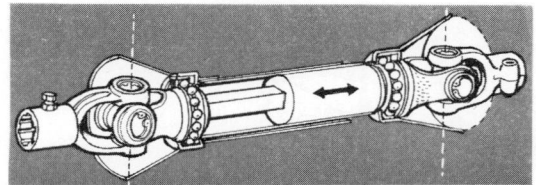

Pins, represented by dotted lines, must be assembled in parallel.

Bevel gear boxes require little attention apart from keeping an eye on the oil level. Overfilling can lead to a lot of trouble with burst oil seals. A gearbox with too much oil builds up a pressure within the housing, caused by the pumping action of the gears. Some gearboxes have special breathers to allow the pressure to escape and

Safety clutches incorporated in the pto drive shaft should be dismantled, cleaned and re-assembled dry. For shafts fitted with shear pins, rather than clutches, it is best to remove the pin and check that the bushing has not seized. This type of safety device may be oiled to ensure it will be free should the pin shear.

Sliding couplings become dry and gummy and should be cleaned off regularly and greased to prevent excessive end loading in the joints.

## OPEN-LINK CHAINS

Open-link chains, widely used on spreaders, must be correctly fitted, especially where the driven sprocket is smaller than the driving sprocket. The rule is: run drive chains with hooks forward and slots to the outside, see Fig 1 (next page). For conveyor chains the bars should be forward and slots outside, see Fig 2 (next page).

Correct chain adjustment is vital. If they are too tight they will cut into the sprocket teeth and put excessive loading through bearings and shafts. If they are too slack they may ride on top of the teeth and whip excessively.

If the links can just be moved from side to side across the sprocket teeth, the tension is about right. If 33 links of any open link chain have worn so much they are one link longer than 33 new links, replace the chain.

Feed conveyor chains must be adjusted to equal tension on both sides or they will run off-centre and cut into the body of the spreader. See that slats are running at right angles to the side boards and are correctly meshed with the drive and idler sprockets. Chain sag should be about 3 per cent of the slack length.

Lubricate them at frequent intervals with a light engine oil. An oil paint-brush makes an ideal applicator, and to ensure the oil runs into the joints it should be applied to the open side of the links. Roller chains are best oiled on the side that contacts the sprocket teeth.

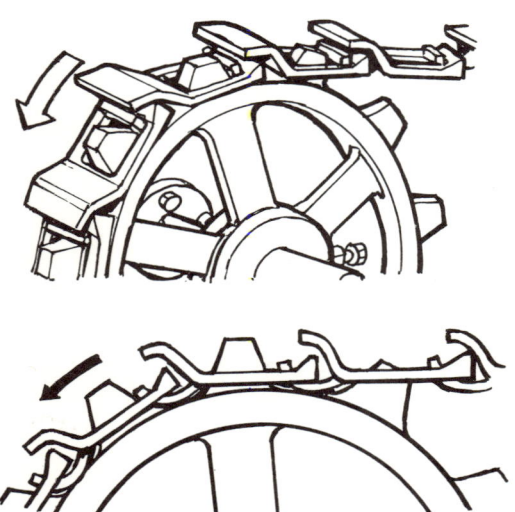

Fig. 1  Hooks forward and slots to the outside on drive chains.

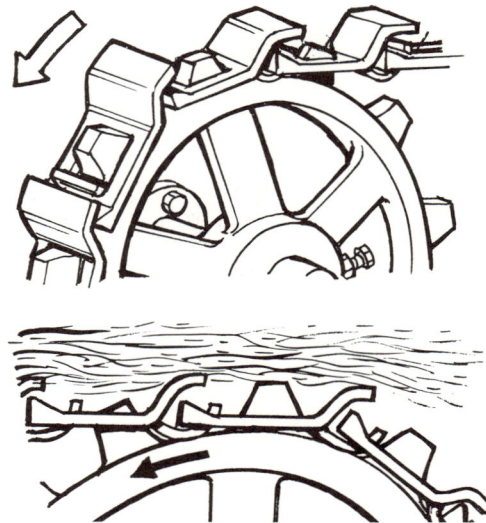

Fig. 2  Bars forward and slots outside on  conveyor chains.

Chain faults; The tensioning sprocket is fitted to the wrong side of the chain thus reducing the number of links in contact with the driving sprocket.

## ROTARY SPREADERS

Rotary type spreaders have now taken a substantial part of the small and medium sized spreader market. They have the advantage of simplicity and very low maintenance. The models from the larger manufacturers are often treated with phosphoric acid before painting, and this can be expected to reduce corrosion significantly.

The secret of good operation of these spreaders is to wrap the chains round the rotor before loading and then load from the ends towards the centre, avoiding over-packing the ends. Initial tear-out by the flails starts from the ends, so make it easy by layering the loading into the rigid flails at the end of the rotor. Putting the centre loads over, behind the rotor, to start off with reduces the load on the rotor and, hence, the power required to get the rotor turning.

Remember that in spreading, the rotary spreader is one of the few implements that may involve a change in pto speed from the standard 540 rpm.

The most likely failure in this machine is fracture of flail chains on the rotor. If these are not replaced an uneven spread and lower rate of work will result. The pto shaft itself and the main drive sprocket and chain should, of course, have regular attention. The rest of the machine is remarkably resistant to neglect but a wash off with a steam cleaner and a thorough check of all parts every season will pay off in longer, trouble-free life.

## REAR UNLOADING SPREADERS

The quality and evenness of spread is governed to a great extent by the efficiency of the shredding cylinders and distributor paddles. If tines are missing or paddles broken off the remaining parts come under increased strain. This kind of over-loading brings about chain and sprocket wear, as well as bearing wear. It also causes lumpy spreading.

Cylinder shaft bearings should be checked for wear, thoroughly cleaned and greased.

Baler twine can damage shafts and bearings, causing overheating in the bearings and melting the grease. Sealed bearings are most vulnerable, the twine wearing away the sealing washers and

Check that shaft securing collars have not worked loose.

leaving them open to liquid and solid manure.

Always start loading at the opposite end to the shredders and fill until the lower cylinder is reached. On no account pile manure on top or force it in and around the shredders. Leaving them clear allows easier starting and reduces the initial strain on the driving mechanism. Loading in this manner gives a more even feed because the manure is more easily separated.

Make it a habit to engage the spreading drive lever before the feed lever. This gives the shredder cylinders time to reach their correct working speed and clear themselves before the main bulk of the load starts moving.

The top shredder cylinder on this machine will do little to help even spreading. The majority of tines are either bent, broken or missing altogether.

In cold weather, make sure that the conveyor chain is not frozen to the bottom of the spreader before loading.

End-of-season maintenance should be done as soon as the last load has been spread and before the muck cakes and hardens. Remember to hose off the parts underneath the body.

Chains should be removed, washed in paraffin and given a coat of heavy grease before being refitted.

Grease the conveyor chain and give spreading gear and the parts where paint has been removed a liberal coating of creosote or old sump oil.

Completely strip the cutter bar, arranging the parts in order after removing all dirt, etc., with a wire brush. Check bar for signs of damage. The points of the fingers should be rounded, not pointed, preferably on a bench grinder. The sides of the fingers and liners are also ground to give a sharp edge to the liners. The aim is a smooth pointed finger and sharp shearing edge for the knife.

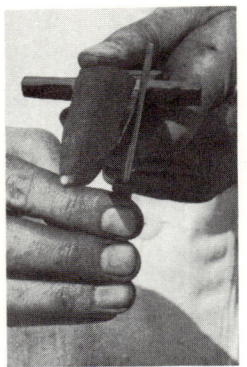

(Left) The angle at each side of the finger should be ground to leave an angle as indicated by the position of the screwdriver. On some makes the finger liner can be replaced and where wear is apparent this may postpone fitting a new finger.

(Right) Wear on the clips should be checked. A new clip (top) is compared with a worn one. This needs replacing because the face has become badly worn, either through wear or damage.

Bent and twisted distributor paddles reduce the effective spreading width.

## OVERHAULS: THE MOWER

In spite of the various alternatives now available to the finger bar type mower, this is still the most widely used and is likely to require more attention than other kinds.

Though different makes of finger bar mower may vary slightly they usually have the same type of cutter bar assembly and method of adjustment and alignment.

The first job is to strip down the entire cutter bar and thoroughly clean this and all parts before checking fingers, wearing plates, ledger plates and clips for wear or damage. The knife will also need to be checked and new sections fitted where necessary, others being sharpened.

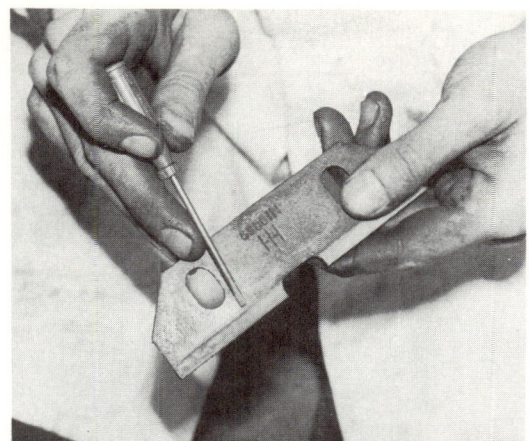

Wearing plates have a slight recess at the leading edge. Check that this is not deepened or extended through wear or poor adjustment when a new part will be necessary.

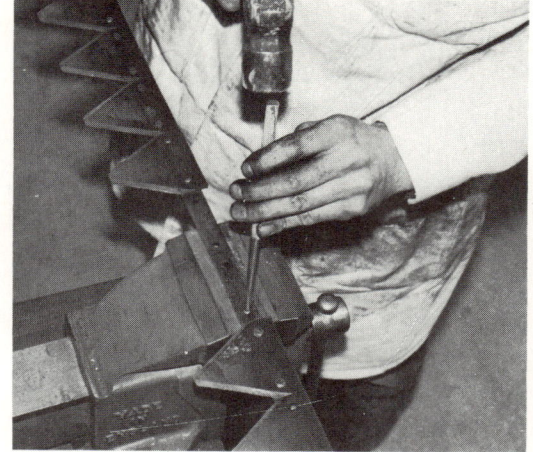

Worn knife sections should be removed by placing the knife back vertically in a vice and giving the rear of the section a sharp blow with a hammer. The rivets are punched out as shown. The rivets on the section nearest the camera have been badly flattened with a hammer and will soon loosen.

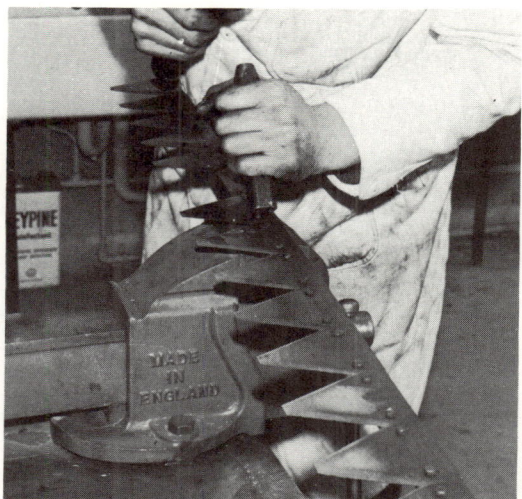

Rivets should be neatly tightened and rounded with a proper punch. This gives a more permanent job than where they are tightened with a hammer. The knife sections must always point away from the worker.

The pictures (page 91—2) illustrate the various points that need attention. Part two of this feature describe (pages 93—4) cutter bar alignment and other points of overhaul and general maintenance for efficient operation.

Having thoroughly overhauled the cutter bar, the knife is replaced and properly bedded down and the cutter bar aligned. Failure to attend to these points will reduce efficiency of the machine and undo much of the work that went into the overhaul. The mower should be fitted to the tractor during this work.

The pitman must run at right angles to the crankshaft and the knife should operate when in work in a straight line with the pitman. The angle can be checked with a straight edge and altered by adjusting the brace and yoke bars. Knife angle can also be corrected by adjusting the mower headstock and, since the fittings vary, it is necessary to check the manufacturer's instruction book for method of adjustment.

Bedding down the knife and alignment of the cutter bar are illustrated on this page. When this has been completed the mower should be greased and the gearbox oil level and drive belts (where fitted) checked.

(Right) The first job is to get the knife to run smoothly without any 'crabbing'. Fingers which are not level can be tapped into position or a tool, consisting of a piece of tube welded to a bar, can be made (as shown here) to ease the fingers into line. Check that fingers are in line by pulling a piece of string across them.

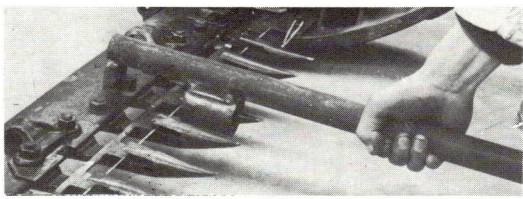

(Left) Check tightness of clips with a postcard. If they are too tight, they can easily be corrected by placing across a vice and lightly tapping with a hammer. On some models shims can be used to adjust the clips. Wearing plates can be adjusted to run level with the knife. Check each one and adjust to correct position so that there is no 'fore and aft' knife play.

(Right) When the knife has been bedded down, check alignment. First, drop a plumb line across the centre of the rear tractor axle and mark the base position on each side.

The tractor is then moved forward, a straight edge put across the two marks and a line drawn in front of the cutter bar. Measuring from the rear edge of the cutter bar to the line at each end will establish the 'lead' which can be adjusted by tightening or slackening the braces or yoke at the headstock. The amount of lead should be **20 mm in 1 metre of cut so that in work the cutter bar runs in a straight line with the pitman.**

Always press the end of the cutter bar back before measuring to take up any play. The mower is then raised on the tractor linkage and the height of the cutter bar measured under each end. The cutter bar should leave the ground horizontally for the first few cm and thereafter the outer end should gain on the inner end so that it is well angled in the raised position. Correction is made by adjusting the tension springs.

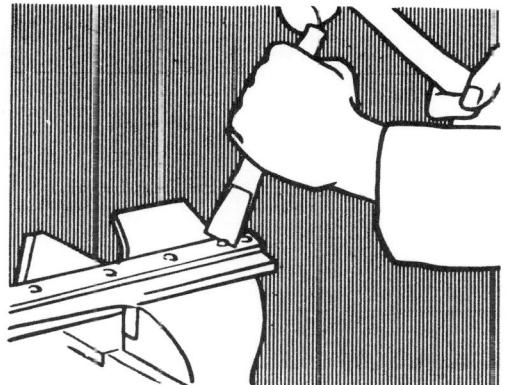

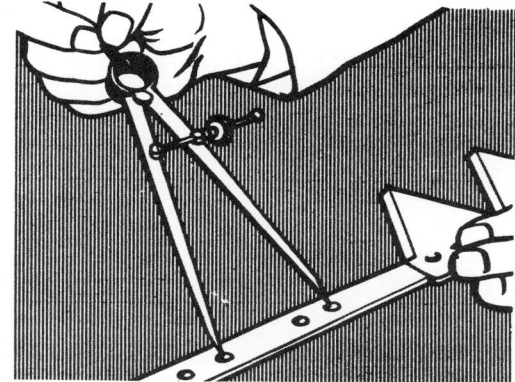

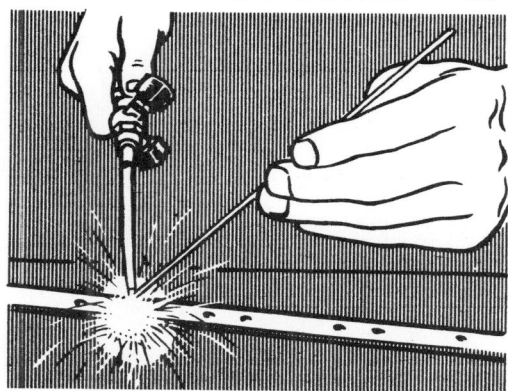

First remove the broken back from the knife head and also two or three sections next to the break on the other piece (left). If the break occurs in the centre of the knife simply remove a few sections on either side of the break. Measure the distance between three holes with dividers to ensure proper spacing (centre). Do this

before welding or heat expansion may cause errors. File broken parts level. Make sure the knife back lies straight when the filed edges are placed together. Weld with a good build-up on both sides (right), preferably using a **No. 5 nozzle with a 2.5 mm dia rod and neutral flame.**

The oxygen cylinder **pressure should be 0.25 bar and the acetylene 0.125 bar.** While the weld is still hot, place the knife back on an anvil and hammer out until the weld has been expended sufficiently to allow a fresh hole to be drilled in the right place.

After the cutting season the knife should be removed and stored with the spare knives. The cutter bar, knives and all working parts should then be covered with grease or a rust preventative compound.

The pitman is designed to protect the knife and drive from damage, but there are occasions when the knife back is broken by stresses in work. A spare knife is usually available, but if replacements are limited it is a reasonably simple matter to weld the broken pieces to avoid renewal and reblading.

Usually the knife back breaks across a hole near the drive end where stress is greatest. The two broken faces must be ground down so they will butt together. Because of this it is vital to lay sufficient weld metal for the join to be hammered out on an anvil so that the new hole can be drilled in the exact place of the original.

The choice of weld rods is between mild steel, silicon manganese or 3 per cent nickel steel. Mild steel is easy to weld but lacks high tensile strength and is likely to break. Silicon manganese

is a more difficult rod to use, but the work produced has an extremely high tensile strength, as has 3 per cent nickel steel. The latter has a high heat tractability so care must be taken in cooling the work.

Silicon manganese is probably the best choice for the farm welder. Properly used, it will result in a lasting repair in which the weld will be stronger than the parent metal. The illustrations above show the repair method using oxy-acetylene equipment.

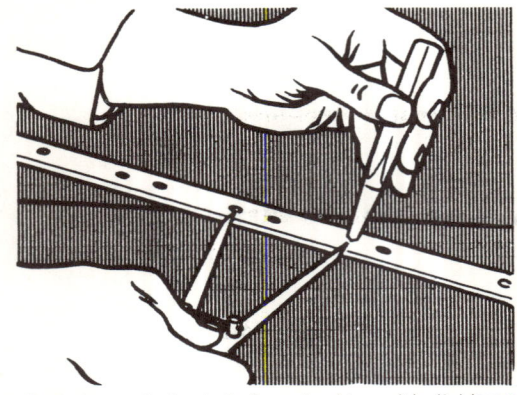
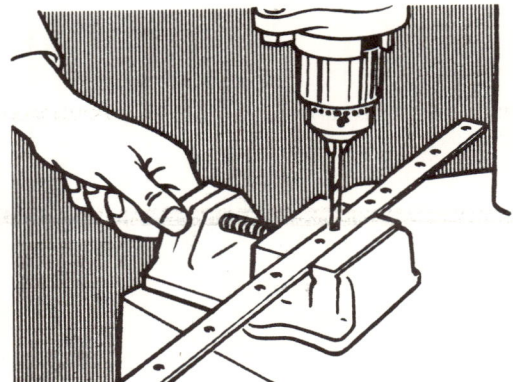

Cool the work slowly before checking with dividers to ensure proper spacing then file off excess weld metal and centre the position for the hole with a punch.
This method ensures that the hole is drilled through the centre of the weld to give maximum strength. Drilling on the edge of the repair may weaken the weld.

## ROTARY MOWER MAINTENANCE

Getting the best from a drum mower depends on two things: careful, skilled driving and good maintenance. These factors are examined here and applied, as an example, to a four drum mower, the Bamford C450.

The basic objective of a mower is to cut while in the working position. So driving should be directed at just that. Run a mower at rated pto speed but only when in working position. Make sure the safety guards are in position. (Even if you don't employ labour, remember that the safety regulations are based entirely on accident statistics.)

The parts that will wear out most rapidly are the cutting blades. Changing a full set takes five minutes or so. Use the knife tool provided to depress the knife retainers. Don't over-do this as it may damage the spring-steel of the retainer. New knives should be fitted with the chamfered edge of the knife upwards.

The saucer under each drum is fitted with a wear plate which actually runs on the ground. This will, eventually, wear out and should be replaced.

The saucer is held on with a single socket screw which can be removed with the allen key provided with the machine. This socket will, on many soils, get clogged up and will need a knife, nail or screwdriver to clean it out before the allen key can be used. The saucer should just pull off but may need coaxing with a soft faced hammer.

Some drum mowers have drain holes in the drums. In the C450 they are in the flat-side of each drum, at the bottom. They should, of course, be kept free.

The main drive belts need seasonal attention and may need replacing. Tensions should be more frequently checked. Adjustment is carried out simply by altering one nut, and its lock-nut, on the tensioner so that the right-angled steel tab under the nuts just touches the main sub-frame.

Slacken the break-away off at the beginning of each season and check that it does actually work. Incidentally, damage may result if the mower is lifted off the ground while the break-away is tripped open.

One of the big advantages of rotary mowers is the reduced maintenance requirement. Normal field work is concerned with greasing and oiling daily with the occasional replacement of blades. The other items raised here are likely to be seasonal or relatively infrequently required during use. In any case, management of the field operation is likely to be much easier if the machine is kept in good order.

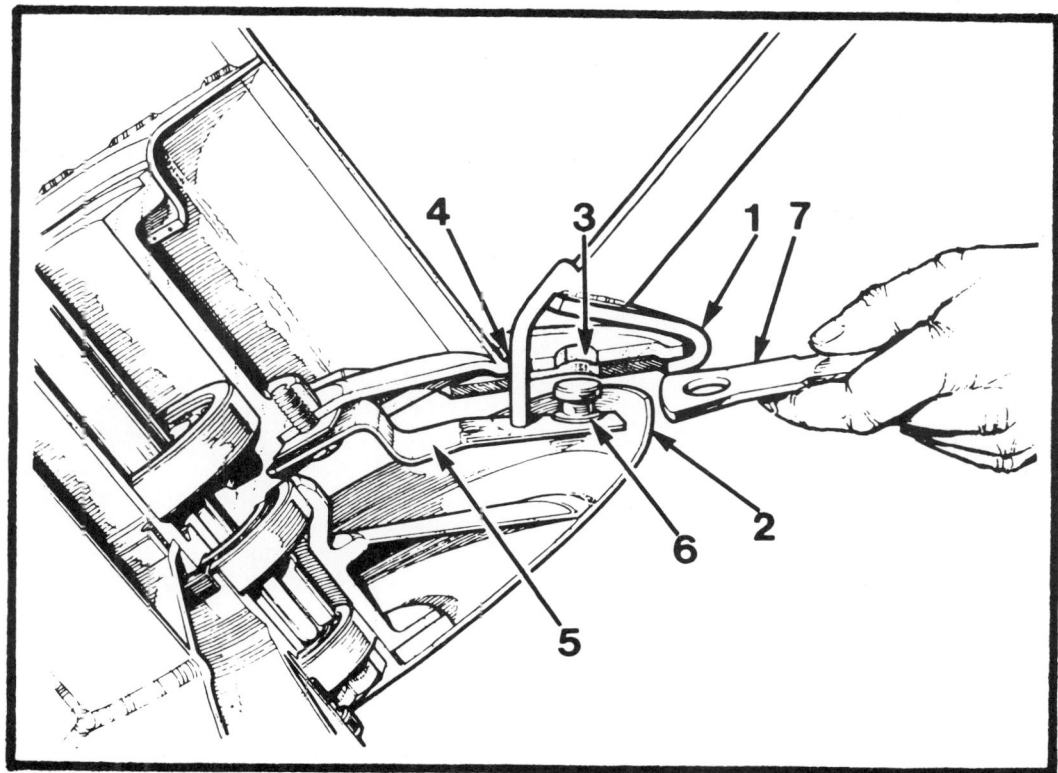

Rotary drum mower — blade replacement
Key: 1 Knife tool, 2 Saucer, 3 Hole for knife retaining stud, 4 Hole for knife tool, 5 Knife retainer spring, 6 Knife retaining stud.

## OVERHAULS: THE ROTARY CULTIVATOR

There are probably 30,000 rotary cultivators on British farms waiting for the soil to dry out. Many will have been dumped in the back of the implement shed just as they were when the weather stopped further autum work. They are hard working machines built to take a severe battering, but they still need maintenance.

This series is based on a Howard E series 60in Rotavator and most hints apply to the rest of the range. For many other models the principles apply by the instruction book should have the final say on details.

Mount the machine on the tractor linkage ensuring first that the mounting plates holding the hitching points are set right for the particular tractor. And, as there are four lower link hitch positions, mountings 1 and 3 or 2 and 4 should be used respectively for either offset or in-line working. Do not splay the links to combine positions 1 and 4.

Detailed settings will be given later. Levelling the machine is the first aim. The rotor and the tractor axle are the guide lines one way; the gearbox is used to decide the front-to-rear level. Adjust the tractor's offside lower link and the top link accordingly.

Use the grease gun with a lithium based grease. Apart from nipples in the universal couplings at both ends of the pto drive shaft there are others on the depth wheel, at the pivot point of the shaft holding it and at the offside rotor bearing. These should be daily jobs during work. Pump in grease until the new stuff shows—except in the rotor bearings. This will take about a dozen pumps of an average gun to fill it then three or four pumps a day.

It is worth pulling apart the two sections of the drive shaft to clean and smear with graphite or molybdenum disulphide grease.

Next check for tightness the castellated nut rather awkwardly situated to hold the drive shaft on the gearbox—particularly if this was not factory fitted when the machine arrived. If it has worked loose the chances are that oil will have leaked past the rubber sealing ring inside and will continue to do so when you have drain-ed, flushed out and refilled the gearbox, which is the next job. Avoid any chance of the gearbox oil draining out of the breather hole by parking the machine properly.

At the same time check the Selectatilth gears. There should be four under the cover, two driving and two 'spares' for changing rotor speeds which fit against the working pair and keep them up to their job. When replacing these cogs, be-

The depth wheel greasing point. The scraper can be adjusted by nuts (A).

Grease the depth wheel arm pivot here. (B) is the drive chain tensioner.

Grease nipple at the offside end of the rotor. (C) is where the blade straightening bar stows and fits the lever the machine. (D) adjusts the skid height.

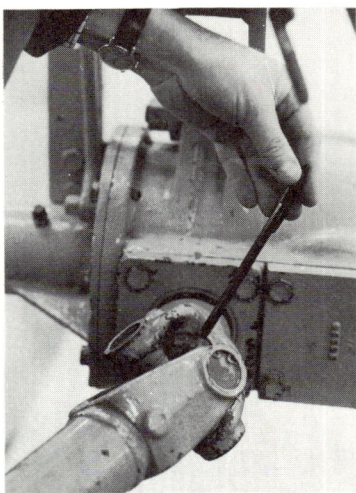

The castellated nut here must be tight... (see next page)

... otherwise the rubber sealing ring (indicated here) will allow the gearbox oil to drain out.

Check position of Selectatilth gears and the spares in the cover. (E) is gearbox oil level.

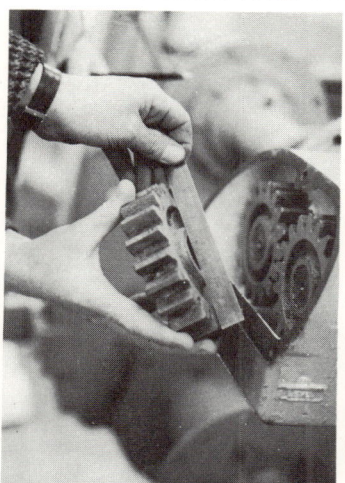

The raised edge of the cogs must face the front of the machine.

Check for **20 mm play** on drive chain by poking with a screwdriver. Turn bolt (F) to adjust.

ware of putting them in the wrong way. One side has a slightly protruding face which should always face forwards. It would work the other way but metal chippings would be ground off into the gearbox.

The encased chain on the nearside which drives the rotor from the top shaft needs attention next. Drain, flush and refill—gearbox and chaincase both take SAE 90 on this machine—and if the case has not been off for 500 hours, remove it and clean it with paraffin.

Chain tension needs checking more often,

however, and with the casing on, this can be done through the inspection plug on the rear side. A screwdriver or a piece of wire pushed against the chain inside will soon show if the correct **20 mm** amount of play takes place. Adjustment can be made on the screw with its locknut on the leading edge of the case.

While the toolbox is this side of the machine, look at the scraper on the depth wheel and adjust the clearance over the wheel by the two bolts in their slotted holes.

The Rotavator must be properly shod. The

right number of blades should be fitted to each flange and each one should be in reasonable condition. If a two-bladed configuration was used to produce a rough winter seed-bed it may be changed to a three-bladed set-up for finer spring work. Alternatively, it is simpler, cheaper and faster to leave the 2 blade rotor and speed it up as necessary with the implement's gear box.

Left-hand blades must lead each pair. This right-handed one is worn but the mark shows when it is time to change.

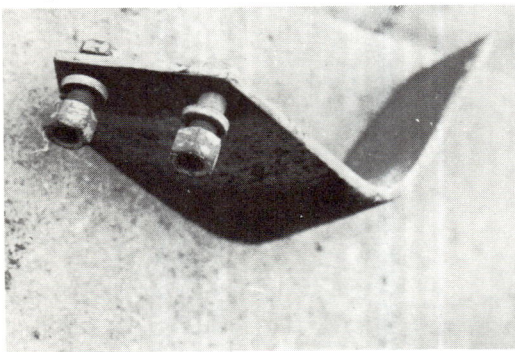

Use the right nuts and bolts for the job and keep them tight.

The makers advise changing all blades at once; 'bumping' will occur in work if some are better than others. So long as a blade has not worn to a point there is still some life in it.

Three main points to remember during re-blading are that the left-hand blade of a pair leads every time, that the 'scroll' pattern across the rotor must be maintained to give the follow-my-leader penetration evenly from side to side, and the blades must be tight.

Howard's freely replace broken, half-worn blades, but not if they have broken through the bolt holes—a sure sign of slack nuts. Use only the proper nuts and bolts— the nuts are long and fine-threaded like car wheel nuts. And put nut and bolt on the right way round, with washer and nut against the rotor flange and the bolt head on the blade side. If blade fitting is a straight replacement job remove one and fit a new one, rather than strip a flange and have to plot the pattern again.

The shanks of some blades may be bent. A special tool supplied with the machine simplifies straightening them. The tool should be kept in the holding tube on the front nearside, for blade straightening should be a daily job.

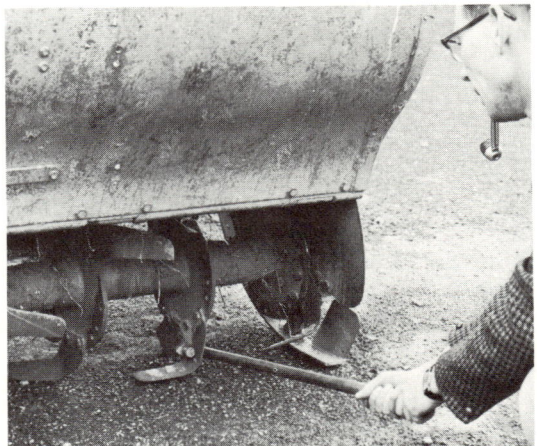

If the shank is bent, straighten it with the bar provided. Otherwise uneven running, extra wear and increased power requirement will result.

For transport, hook the cover right up, using the hook on the cover itself. Height for work is set using the chain in the spring-loaded-slot (A).

The blade straightening bar can also be used to help move the machine for hitching-up.

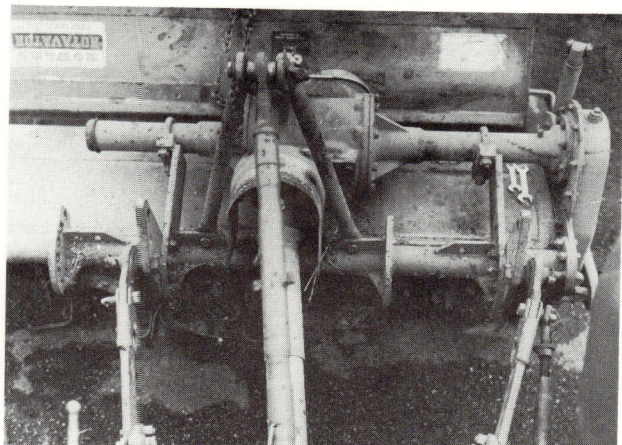

The four mounting points can be seen. Here 1 and 3 are in use for offset work, 2 and 4 are for in-line working.

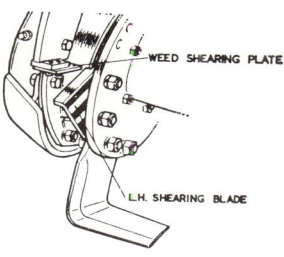

WEED SHEARING PLATE

L.H. SHEARING BLADE

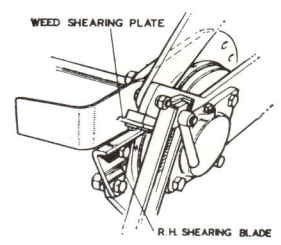

WEED SHEARING PLATE

R.H. SHEARING BLADE

The shield is not just a safety cover. Its position plays a vital part in the state of the final tilth. Oil the hinges and make sure the spring-loaded slot which holds the check chain is in good order. Hold the shield in place with the top clip to reduce shock loads during transport.

On the flange at each end of the rotor are the weed shearing blades designed to prevent rubbish wrapping round. They fit any pair of bolt holes to suit the blade formation. The fixed shearing plates, are slotted and two set-screws each side

need slackening to allow the plates to be adjusted to just clear the cutters.

Finally, give a rub down and grease the three hitch points to make coupling up easier, and run a spanner over all the nuts. Recommended order of hitching is top link, nearside lower link and then, using the blade straightening bar as a lever, the offside lower link can usually be kicked into position. For safety have the pto out of gear and the tractor switched off before coupling up the shaft.

Fit the stabiliser bars on the machine's mounting pins, raise the linkage and fix the other ends on the tractor. If chains are used tighten to limit side sway to 25 mm.

The top link should be adjusted so that with the blades on the ground the gearbox is horizontal. Level off across the machine by winding down the depth wheel until the blades are just clear, then wind the tractor's offside lower link adjuster so that blade clearance is equal right across.

The skid on the opposite side to the depth wheel should be set to run about 25 mm above the finished work. It is not a depth control skid and is simply there to prevent the blades digging in too far if the depth wheel drops in a hole on uneven ground.

To rub home the message of the previous pages on overhaul, the following photos show some expensive reminders of what can happen when maintance is slack or the machine is misused. The same principle applies to many machines on the farm.

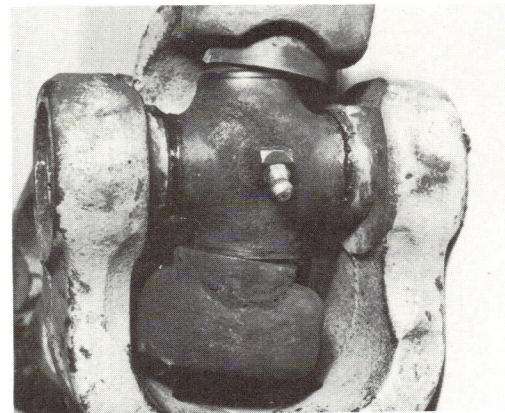

The universal joint collapsed through lack of proper lubrication. The left and right bearings were greased but it was not forced through the top and bottom ones which have broken down.

This damaged gearbox was caused when the top stays were allowed to work loose.

This back plate was twisted when the machine was turned in work without lifting it out.

Lack of lubrication has caused the needle rollers to disintegrate and the clutch drive plate yoke took the full force of the misalignment.

This damaged crown wheel was caused by faulty clutch setting. The tension nuts should have been tightened until each spring was compressed 4 mm measured between the sheet metal cover and the flat washer to give a breakaway torque of 1,356 Nm.

# OVERHAULS: THE HYDRAULIC COUPLING

The most common fault with external hydraulic couplings is leaking valves, especially where slack maintenance has allowed the oil to become dirty. New 'O' rings and valve sleeves can be fitted on the farm, and will save several pounds on replacing the complete coupling.

No special tools are needed. Parts required are a new valve sleeve and 'O' ring for the tractor coupling, and a new 'O' ring and valve for the implement coupling.

To repair a tractor coupling, remove the valve from the fitting bracket by unscrewing the oil pipe and slackening off the locking nut. Then clean the valve in a suitable solvent, such as paraffin, before removing the spring locking clip se-

curing the valve assembly with a pair of long-nosed pliers. Turn the screw clockwise to release the valve, which is removed from the other end of the coupling. Take out the valve sleeve and spring at the same time and clean thoroughly.

Then fit the new valve sleeve and 'O' ring. The 'O' ring will slip easily into the groove on the valve sleeve if it is smeared with soft soap.

Don't forget that the valve screw has to be

The coupling must be throughly cleaned to prevent any trace of dirt getting into the inside of the valve assembly before it is replaced.

Remove the coupling from the tractor by disconnecting the oil pipe and slackening the lock nut next to the carrying bracket.

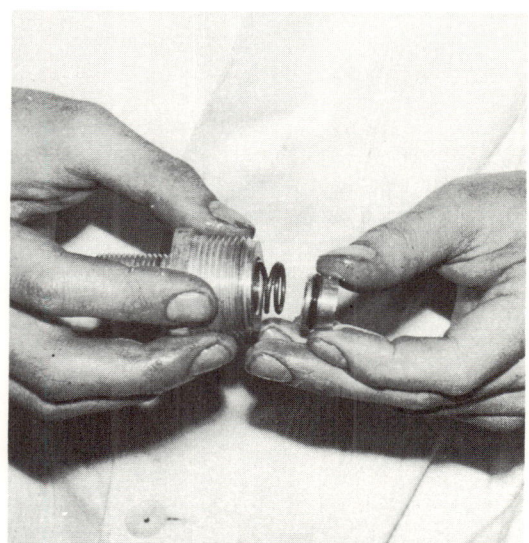

The new 'O' ring is fitted to the valve sleeve and the spring and sleeve replaced in the valve body.

turned anti-clockwise when re-fitting. Make sure the spring locking clip has been replaced before the coupling is fitted back to the tractor.

To work on an implement coupling, take the female coupling from the trailer or implement, and remove the small Allen screw on the side of the rounded part of the body. Then put the coupling in the vice, and use a pair of circlip pliers to unscrew the threaded insert from the valve body. There is a special tool for this job, but circlip pliers are a good second best.

The two halves of the coupling can then be unscrewed by hand to release the valve assembly and pressure spring contained inside. Clean all parts thoroughly.

The 'O' ring can be seen in the bottom of the round section of the coupling. Take it out with a small screwdriver, and fit the new 'O' ring after soaping it. This done, fit the new valve and reassemble the coupling.

In both cases, the entire operation need take no longer than an hour—usually far less—and the result will be a valve coupling that should see plenty more action.

The trailer end coupling has an Allen key in the side. This is removed before the coupling is placed in a vice and a pair of circlip pliers used to unscrew the threaded insert from the valve body.

## OVERHAULS: THE UNIVERSAL JOINT

Gradual wear, accelerated by mis-alignment, will cause the universal joints used in pto drive shafts to become slack. If this is not attended to the bearings will break up and the coupling itself may be badly damaged.

The renewal of bearings and cross shaft is not difficult and can be quickly carried out. The new parts required are a cross piece, containing the grease nipple, which supports the two halves of the coupling, and four new cups containing needle bearings, one for each knuckle of the joint. When these parts have been fitted the coupling will be serviceable for a further period of use and costly replacement of the entire coupling will have been postponed.

The job of replacing the worn parts in a universal joint is illustrated in the pictures on the next page.

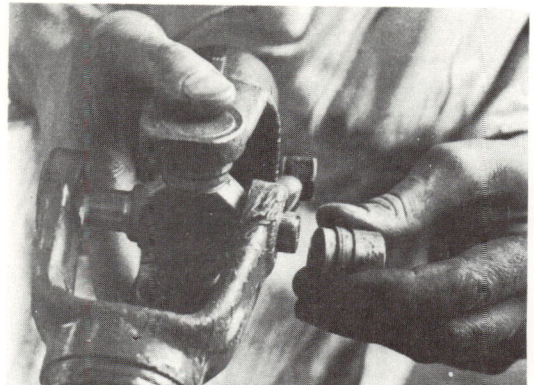

1  Place the universal coupling in a vice and remove the spring clips from each side of the knuckles on the universal joint. Cups are pushed partly out of the yokes by placing one yoke across the vice and tapping the other yokes with a hammer. The large yoke is more cumbersome and should be removed first, before the cross piece is similarly placed across the vice (as above) and the cups driven in turn from the smaller yoke.

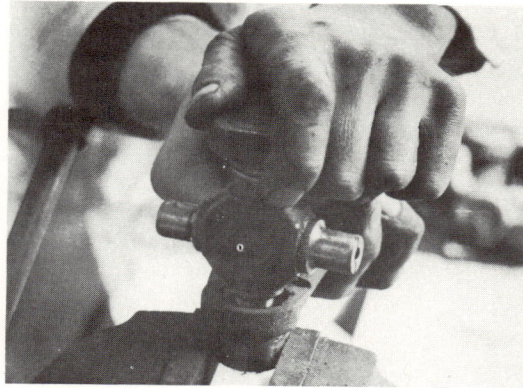

3  Lay out the replacement parts on a clean surface and grease the inside of the cups to retain the needle bearings. Take the new cross piece and push one section well into one of the holes on the smaller yoke from the inside. One of the cups is then gently run on as illustrated.

2  When each cup has been exposed it is gripped in the vice and removed by twisting and pulling the coupling. Next, clean off both yokes and drive one of the old cups through each hole to remove dirt and burrs.

5  A spacer is then inserted between the cup and the vice jaw, which is tightened again to press the cup further into the yoke. This pushes the cross piece well into the opposite hole to facilitate fitting the next cup. When this is pressed home in the vice the cross piece is centred and both cups will fit flush with the sides of the yoke.

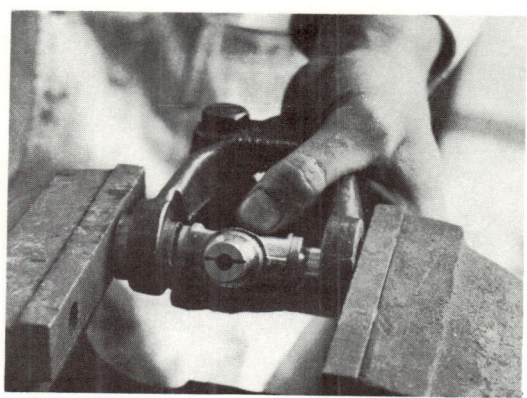

4  With the cup in position, place the coupling in the vice and tighten to press the cup into the coupling jaw until it is a flush fit.

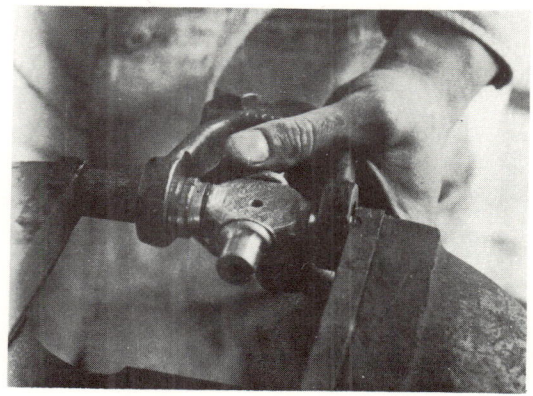

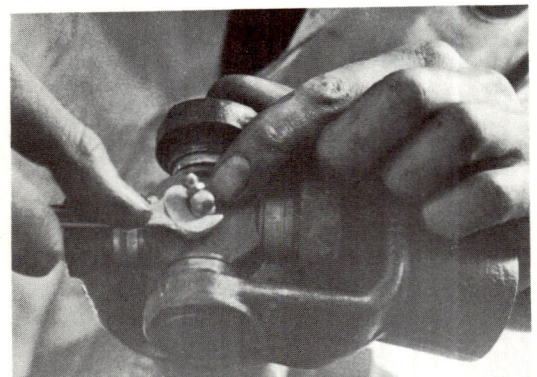

6  The grease nipple is then fitted and the spring clips replaced. Care should be taken to fit the cross piece so that the grease nipple faces outwards when the assembly is complete. Never over-grease the universal joints or the seal will be damaged.

## OVERHAULS: THE BALER SLIP-CLUTCH

The flywheel slip-clutch is the primary safety device of the baler. It protects the machine from gradual overload and prevents serious damage.

Its principle is to limit the amount of torque supplied by the pto. If it slips too soon the baler output is reduced, and if it does not slip overloading of the baler results and a twisted bale chamber may arise, causing a long delay.

The lay-out of the clutch is that the machined surface of the driven member is trapped by two circular friction linings between spring-loaded pressure plates,. The torque input to the baler is governed by the compression of the individual springs. Most manufacturers recommend in their instruction booklets a minimum length the springs should be compressed and this figure should be closely followed.

Main causes of trouble to check are broken springs, rusted linings, oil or grease on the linings. To inspect these parts properly the unit should

Foreground, drive plate dogs sheared off. Background, badly-worn dogs should be replaced.

Worn clutch plates—one with the centre twisted out.

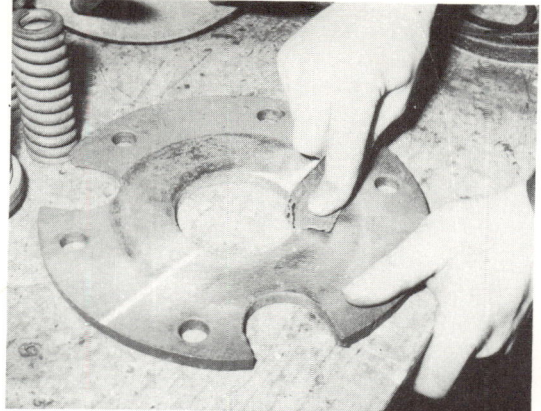

Cleaning up pressure plates with emery cloth to remove rust and pitting.

Check slip-clutch torque with a spring balance on a bar 60 mm from the pto joint.

be dismantled by removing the over-run clutch first. If the driven member is badly damaged it will need renewing as will the linings and perhaps the springs.

After servicing and replacement of worn or damaged parts take care to re-assembly correctly, tighten each nut up on the springs equally and fit the unit back on to the flywheel.

Next set the torque to the manufacturers' recommendation figure, e.g., several Sperry New Holland models require a torque of 270 Nm.

To check clutch action, place a wrench on the baler pto (power take off) shaft and lock the flywheel or the plunger. If the clutch is operating properly, a force of 45 kg (100 lb) applied on the handle of the wrench at a point 60 cm (24in) from the centre of the pto shaft should cause the clutch to slip. If the clutch slips too easily tighten each nut equally in turn until the correct torque is obtained.

A final check should be made after the baler has been in work for a while to ensure that the clutch is not unduly hot.

## SHARPENING AND RESETTING BALER KNIVES

The knives in the bale chamber work hard, making about 70—80 cuts per minute. Before the baling season they should be removed and sharpened on the grindstone.

Take care when sharpening not to over-heat the blade or it will lose its hardness and quickly become blunt when put to work. Grind off a little at a time, cooling the blade frequently in a bucket of water.

Keep the blade angle as near as possible to that of the original and keep the edge straight. Small notches in the blade caused by stones or wire can be removed by grinding the whole blade back till the edge is straight. Large chips from the knife edge can be filled in only by welding and resharpening by a specialist.

Some balers have a shear bar instead of a stationary knife. This should be removed and sharpened as its shearing edge will become rounded after a season's work. Grind it back to its original profile.

Next refit the stationary knife or shear bar and set the ram-knife parallel to it until there is about one thirty-second of an inch clearance. This clearance is critical. Too much will give a rough-edged bale and consume more power and too little will cause the knives to hit each other.

*Pictures by courtesy of Rycote Wood College, Thame.*

While removing and refitting the knife and checking the clearance, wedge the flywheel to prevent it turning or get someone to hold it, otherwise the ram may move along the bale chamber and cause serious hand injuries.

Shims are used to help set the clearance. They are thin strips of metal placed behind the knife. By adding a shim or taking one away, the clearance can be set accurately.

Two types are made for baler knives. One is a long shim that fits the length of knife and the other is a small, short shim used at the ends to ensure that it is parallel with the other knife.

To get an accurate setting it may be necessary to add and subtract shims. Check several times, tightening up the screws each time. Check clearance at each end of the knife with feeler gauge.

## OVERHAULS: STUBBORN BEARINGS

A bearing should slide easily on and off the shaft, and in and out of its housing. This seldom happ-

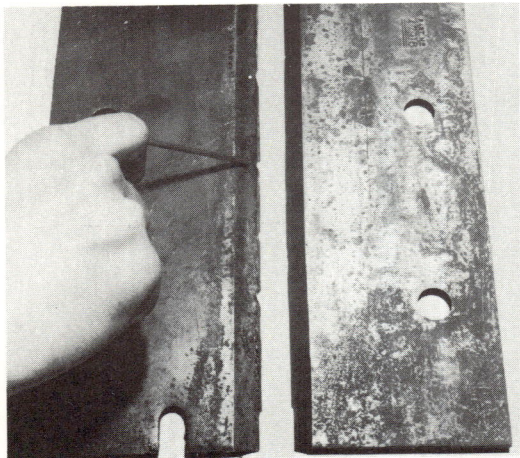

Damage caused to a knife by stones entering baler.

How to position shims in relation to the knife.

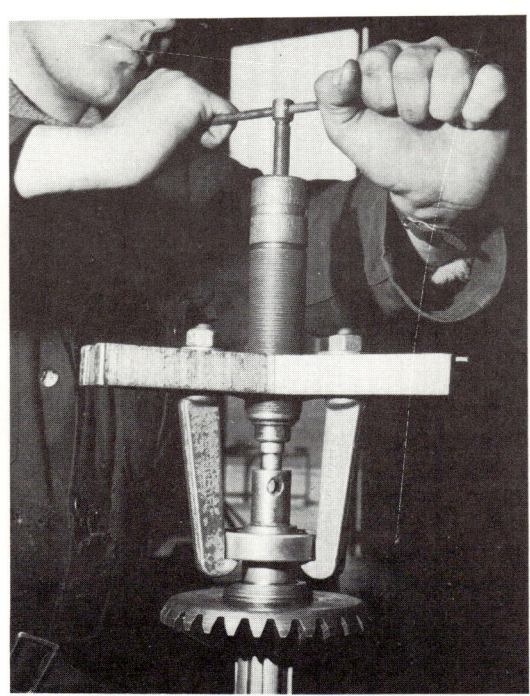

The best way to remove a tight bearing—with a puller.

ens as burrs, rust and dirt help to made removal difficult.

If a bearing will not come off easily because of spreading on the end of the shaft use a file and emery cloth to remove the excess metal. A set of bearing pullers, which pull the bearing off the final 10 or 20 mm is usually supplied with two or three different-sized sets of legs. If no pullers are available, two tyre levers placed behind and on opposite sides of the bearing may help. Give the levers sharp taps with a hammer in turn to try to move it.

Remember, the pullers or tyre levers must be positioned behind the inner race of the bearing. Clean up any damage and grease the shaft well before fitting a new bearing.

*Pictures by courtesy of Rycote Wood College, Thame.*

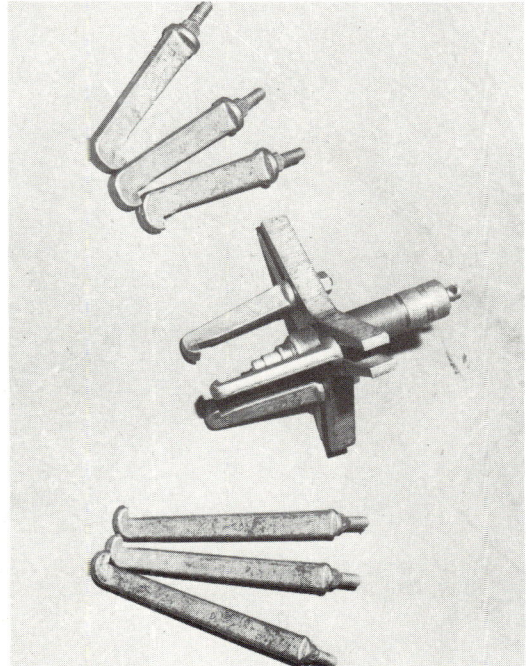

A puller with three sets of legs.

Gas-cut a bearing from a shaft if all other methods fail.

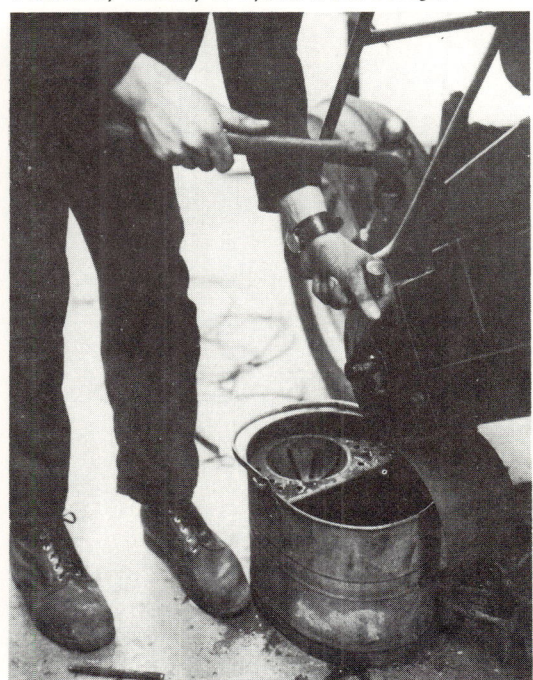

After making the second cut, use a chisel to split the race.

If filing, levers or pullers will not budge the bearing, gas-cut it from the shaft. The problem is to cut the bearing without damaging the shaft. First cut off the outer race, taking care not to burn any plastic, wood, or rubber in the area of the bearing.

The second cut must be across the width of the inner race. Aim to cut through half the thickness of the race, so that the flame does not touch the shaft.

Use a chisel and hammer on the half-cut to split the race and it will slide off the shaft.

# FARM WELDING

### THE BASIC ESSENTIALS

The fully-equipped workshop has both gas and electric arc equipment. To do in the easiest way all the jobs that crop up could mean a capital outlay of £500 to £600.

It is possible, however, for as little as £100 to £150—less for second-hand equipment—to obtain a gas or electric welding kit sufficient to tackle most farm workshop jobs. If both gas and electric can be justified so much the better; arc welders are more quickly set up and more easily used for awkward jobs inside and underneath machines, whereas gas is better for high temperature and tricky low temperature work. When it is a choice between the two there are a number of points to be considered.

For the man who is quick to pick up workshop skills the electric type is probably the better bet—particularly where the equipment is needed for welding only. A 150 to 200 amp arc welder—large enough for most farm jobs—can be bought for £100 to £150, the same price as a new gas welding kit.

Gas welding, on the other hand, is more flexible, since it makes possible a number of jobs apart from welding.

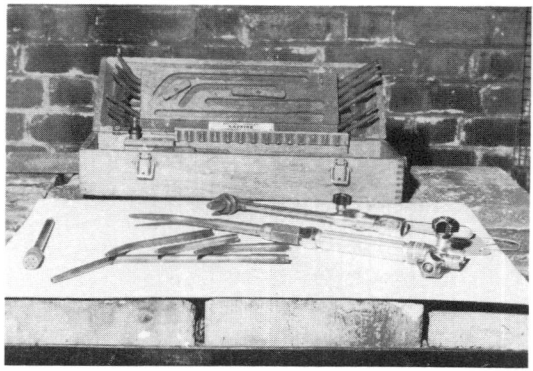

The front torch of this gas welding kit is the standard tool and will take the full range of nozzles. The torch at the back is for cutting. The large nozzle, far left, is for metal heating.

Oxy-acetylene equipment can be used for high speed metal cutting and for low temperature work like brazing and bronze welding. It also forms a convenient source of concentrated heat for jobs like tine straightening and light forging.

Electric arc sets can, in some situations, be used for the lighter low temperature work by the use of the carbon arc technique.

The basic technique for welding mild steel with both types of equipment can be learnt by the average tractor driver in a short time at a county college course. On balance, proficiency in gas welding is probably more difficult to achieve than electric arc welding. With either method,

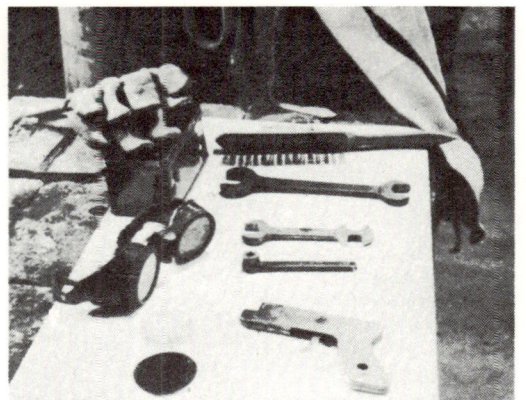

Essentials for use with gas welding tackle: a flint lighter, valve key, union spanner and large spanner for fitting valve gauges to bottles. Wire brush for cleaning. Goggles, which must always be worn. Leather gloves and apron for protection.

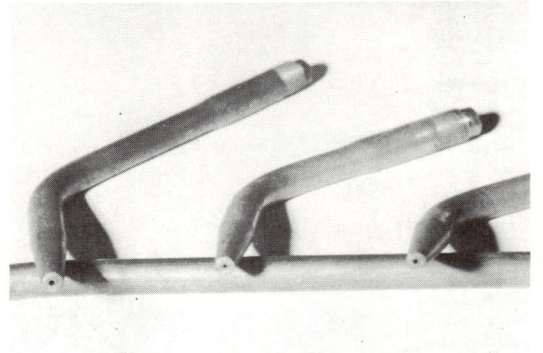

The three most commonly used nozzles are from left to right: No. 25, for welding metal in the 6 to 8 mm thickness range, No. 3 for very thin metal and No. 9 for 3 mm thick plate.

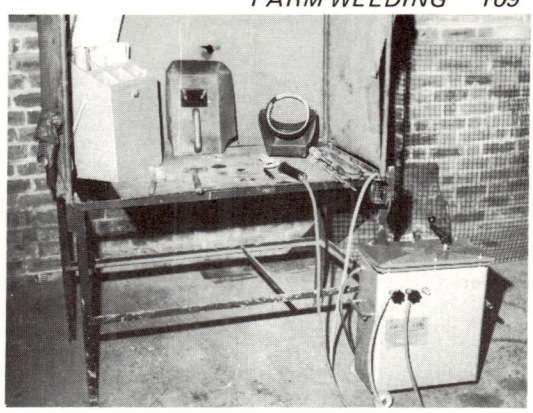

This 200 amp a.c. electric arc welding machine gives sufficient power for most farm jobs. The welding table is fitted with a steel plate top and flash screens. For gas welding the plate is replaced by firebricks.

practice makes perfect, so stick to the simpler jobs to begin with—someone's life maybe at risk if a job s not properly done.

Equipment needed apart from the welding tackle itself will be special spanners, wire brushes, protective shields or goggles and a leather apron and gloves for the heavy work. For the smaller, lighter jobs a proper welding table is most useful and can be made in the farm workshop.

The table is easily made from 38 mm angle iron using the welding kit (see page 115). For gas welding it should be made to hold 230 x 100 mm

fire-bricks which are much cheaper than the larger blocks normally sold for this purpose, to give a good safe welding and heating surface.

As a good electrical contact between the job and the earth side of the welder is essential for arc welding, the table top for this type of work should be made of 6 mm plate. The larger job can be done on the fire-bricks with the earth lead from the welder attached directly to the job—in the same way that direct work on a machine would be done. Where both types of welding are used the plate top can be removable. At all times, make sure that there are no oil rags, cans of pet-

rol, or other combustible materials in the close vicinity.

When used for electric welding the table must be fitted with a flash screen—temporary or even permanent blindness is possible from only momentary exposure to arc light at close quarters. The screen must be of fire-proof material stretched over a 25 mm tubing frame which will fit into sockets at the corner of the table.

So, for a capital cost of as little as £150 and the investment of some time in learning how to use the equipment, you are set up to do a whole host of repairs which cost much more when done by

outsiders—not counting the cost of the time
wasted while waiting for the job to be done. In
the next few pages we will explain the basic
techniques of both types of welding and the out-
lines of some more difficult jobs.

BASIC GAS WELDING

To ensure easy working and safety, oxyacetylene
welding equipment must be handled, set up and
adjusted in the correct manner. Oxygen and
acetylene bottles must be handled and firmly
fixed in an upright position (1)—either to the
side of the welding table or in a wheeled trolley
stand.

Before fitting the gauges blow the sockets
clean by opening and closing the bottle valves
quickly; this ensures a gastight seat for the gauge
connections (2). The bottles are colour coded—
amber acetylene, black oxygen. To make doubly
sure that there can be no mistakes all acetylene
connections are left-hand thread and those on
the oxygen right-hand thread.

The gauges are screwed in hand tight and then
taken up a further half turn with the correct
spanner. Before lighting the welding torch test
the system for leaks. With the gauge valves turned off, switch on the bottle valves one turn and
set the left-hand working pressure gauges to between 0.138 and 0.345 bar. Note gas pressure in
the cylinders on the right-hand gauge, then switch
off the bottle valve. If the gauge units are in good

1

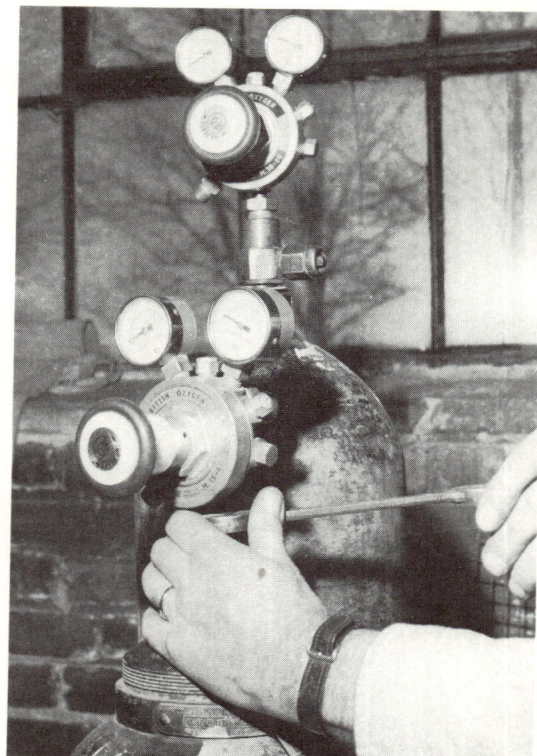

2

order and are properly connected to the bottles,
the needles should not move: if they do the
seatings are dirty or the units need reconditioning.

Next, connect the piping—it comes in 4.5 m
lengths which can be doubled with a connector
for jobs a long way from the bottles—making

sure that the flame traps (clearly marked 'blow-pipe') are on the torch end (3). Connect the torch to the other end of the piping—still following the colour coding. Select the correct nozzle for the thickness of metal to be welded (4) and attach it to the torch. Before tightening the union nut make sure that the end is firmly seated in the torch socket.

The nozzle must be set at the correct angle for easy working. Hold the torch in the working hand (5) so that the valve taps are well clear of the inside of the wrist and allow completely free movement, and set the nozzle at an angle of about 60 degrees from the horizontal before tightening the union nut (A) with a spanner.

## LIGHTING UP

Having ensured that the oxy-acetylene welding equipment is correctly set up for easy and safe working, you are now ready to light up.

It is most important to set the flame properly—there must be the right balance of acetylene and oxygen and no gap between the flame and the tip of the nozzle.

With both the gas and the acetylene gauges

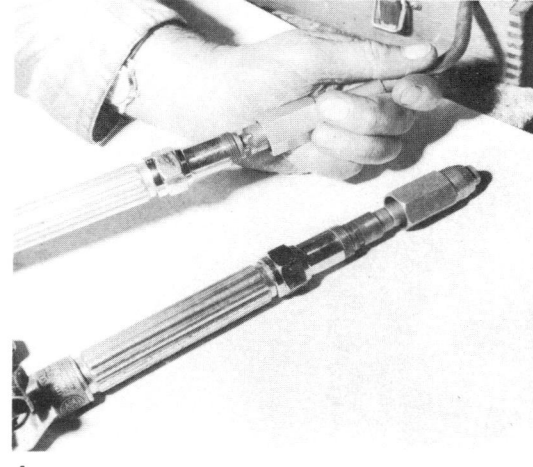

4

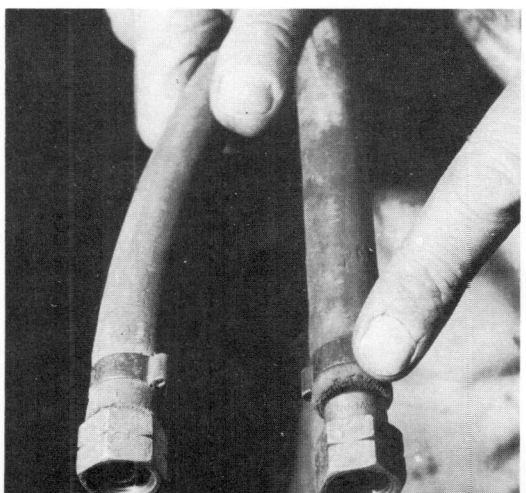

3

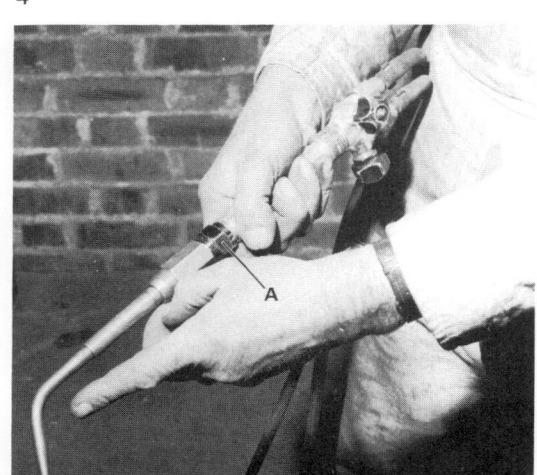

5

1

2

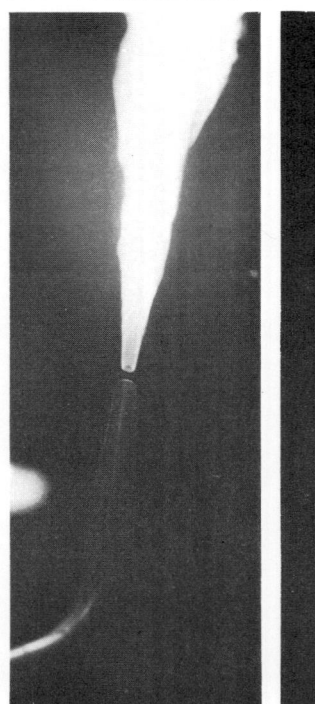

**3**

**4**

set at between 0.138 and 0.345 bar (1), turn on the acetylene and ignite, then turn up the gas on the torch valve until just above the point at which the flame smokes (2). The flame must not be separated from the nozzle tip (3). Now turn on the oxygen slowly until the dark blue and the light blue flame cones coincide to give a fine, sharp, bright 6 to 9 mm 'neutral' flame (4).

Hold the torch with the nozzle at 60 to 70 degrees to the work and the rod at 30 to 40 degrees (5). Both must be in line with the weld.

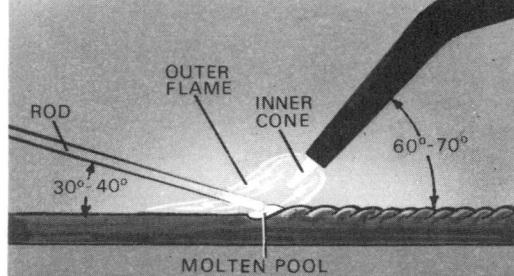

**5**

The aim is to keep a pool of molten metal under the torch by moving it slightly from side to side to ensure that both sides of the join are being heated and to feed in the weld metal under the flame point by a steady in-and-out movement of the rod.

Select your welding rod according to the thickness of metal to be welded (6). The rods (illustrated) are: 4 mm for metal up to 1 mm; 2.5 mm for 2 to 3 mm and 3 mm for 3 to 6 mm. The pieces of metal to be welded should be placed the same distance apart as their thickness and tacked at each end by melting the two edges and dipping in the welding rod. Welding proceeds from right to left (7) (see next page) and the two edges should be positioned so that there is a slight V-

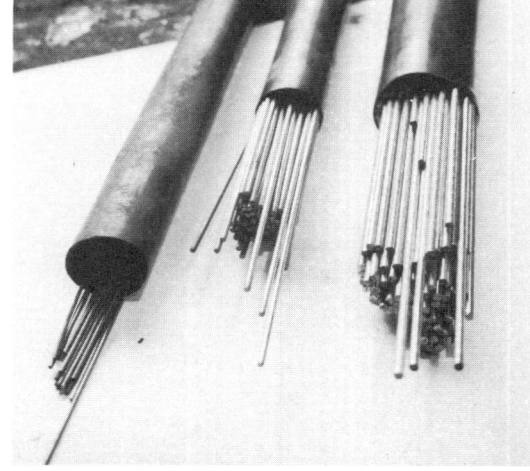

**6**

shape between them in a leftward direction, to allow for contraction of the joint as the metal gets hot

7

## ELECTRIC ARC WELDING

Electric arc welding consists in passing a high amperage, low voltage, electric current through the piece of metal to be welded and, by making the current jump or 'arc' from one contact—the welding rod or 'electrode'—to the metal, causing great heat to be concentrated on it. This has the same effect as a gas welding flame but, because the welding rod is part of the apparatus, only one hand is needed for the job.

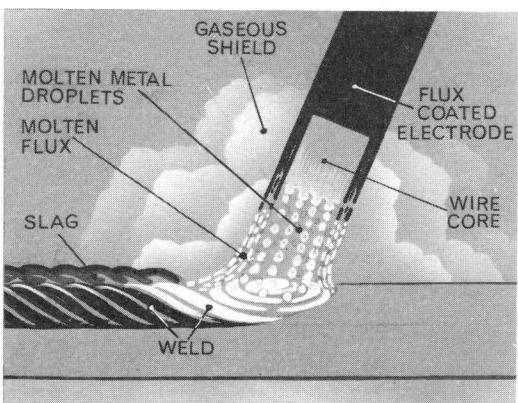

Electric welding proceeds from left to right and the flux surrounding the welding rod forms a protective cover on the metal as it cools. This is 'slag' chipped off when the job is finished.

The electric arc forms a pool of molten metal in exactly the same way as a gas flame, and the molten metal which fuses with the two edges of the job comes from the combined welding rod and 'torch'. There is a risk of contamination of the molten metal—which could weaken the joint—by some components of atmospheric air, so the welding rod is protected by a coating of flux which melts with the metal and forms another protective cover on the weld until it cools (diagram). This solidified cover hardens and is

1

easily chipped off with a slag hammer when the job is completed.

The basic arc welding set-up (1) includes the earth side of the welder which is connected to the metal top of the table by the spring-loaded earth strap (extreme right), and the welding 'torch,' the hand grip (right centre). The eyes are protected from the fierce glare by either the hand-held shield (rear centre) or the head clip type shield (rear right). The slag hammer (left centre) is used to chip off the deposit left by the flux on the weld and the wire brush must be used to clean the joint before welding.

There are usually two alternative voltage connections on the welding unit (centre left) (2). Low voltage allows higher amperage and is safer. High voltage reduces the amperage range but allows easier maintenance of the arc and higher heat at any given amperage. Finer amperage adjustments are made with the handle, which registers the set amperage on the dial (by the operator's left-hand fingers). The amperage is set according to the thickness of the welding rod (or 'electrode'); typical examples are 20-30 amps for 1.6 mm, 100-130 amps for 3.2 mm and 175-230 amps for 5 mm. Correct amperages are marked on welding rod packets.

The thickness of the electrode or welding rod is selected according to the thickness of metal to be welded (3). Typical examples would be 3.2 mm rods for 6 to 7 mm thick metal and 4.0 mm rods for 9 to 12 mm thick metal.

2

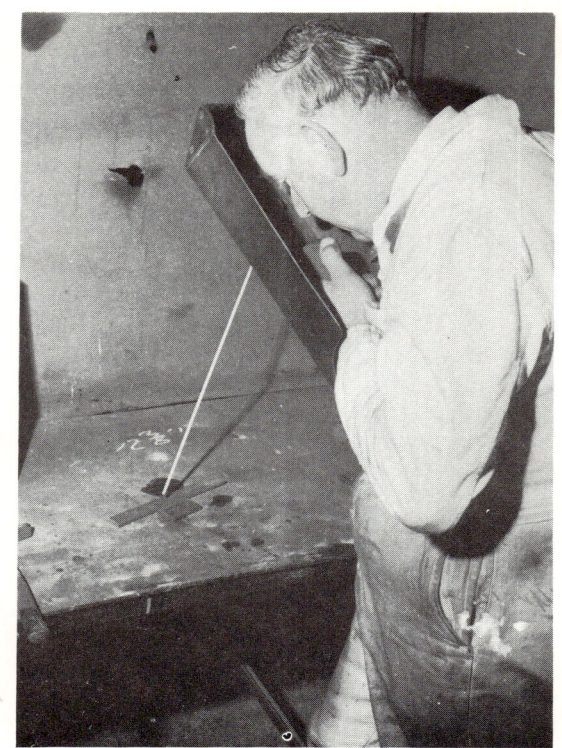

3

The rod is held at an angle of 80 degrees and the hand must be lowered towards the work as the welding rod or electrode melts away, to maintain the tip at the same distance from the work (4). The angle of the rod is increased as the thickness of the rod increases. Otherwise the operation is the same.

Before starting work set the welder to the correct amperage for the size of the welding rod in use. The two pieces of metal are tacked together as for gas welding and the welding proceeds from left to right.

Brace the right-hand side of the body against the side of the welding table, to help steady the hand. Strike an arc by touching the end of the rod quickly on the work—the action should be like that of striking a match. Draw off and maintain the rod 2 or 3 mm from the work. This needs practice; you will weld the electrode to the work several times before you get the knack. When this happens remove the welding handle quickly from the rod and knock it off with the slag hammer.

A steady hand is probably more important with electric than with gas since the electrode must be kept steadily at the right distance from the metal as it burns away.

Before the arc is struck the eye-shield must be moved in front of the eyes; never strike an arc with the eyes uncovered, as painful temporary blindness can result. This precaution also applies to helpers and onlookers.

4

## MAKING A TABLE

To show oxyacetylene welding equipment being used for a practical job, we show the step by step construction of a welding table.

The main materials are 32 mm steel angle iron for the frame and 32 mm T-section for the internal supports of the firebrick table top—see cutting list (page 117).

After cutting to length, the main job is welding up the table top. Simplest way of joining the corners is a butt joint (see 1 overleaf). A 45 degree join is neater but more difficult. Before the joint can

be welded the edges must be ground back to give a 60 degree included angle between the two edges (2) to ensure that the weld penetrates right into the joint.

1

2

The joint is welded on the underside to leave the top flush for the bricks to seat properly. Lay the two pieces—held upright by clamps—on a bench and make sure that they are at right angles (3) before welding.

3

The secret of a job like this is to have sufficient heat to warm up the metal quickly and to be able to work quickly without burning the metal —so use a no. 9 nozzle.

To prevent expansion distorting the joint, the two edges of the weld must be 'tacked' before starting the weld proper. But before tacking, heat up the metal for a few seconds (4) with a neutral flame (see page 111)—this will also be used for the job. Get a molten pool at the edge and then just dab in the welding rod briefly and then, after re-checking with the set square, repeat the process on the other edge of the joint (5).

4

5

The welding then proceeds (6) (see next page) following the drill shown in the basic technique as described on pages 114—115. The rest of the table top is then welded up by joining the T-section pieces at 25 cm centres into the frame. Straight butt welds are used to attach the legs— with regular checking with the set square—to the table top. A frame similar to the top, but 12 mm shorter and narrower is constructed for the leg stays and is welded into the angle of the legs. Fitting the firebricks into the channels completes the job.

6

### Welding Table-Cutting List

| | |
|---|---|
| Two pieces 32 mm angle | 610 mm long |
| Two pieces 32 mm angle | 1,210 mm long |
| Two pieces 32 mm angle | 595 mm long |
| Two pieces 32 mm angle | 1,190 mm long |
| Four pieces 32 mm T-section | 610 mm long |
| Four pieces 32 mm angle | 760 mm long |

## CUTTING OUT DETAILS

Cutting-out details and sizes of the parts to make a table are the same for arc welding as shown in the article on gas welding. Joints can be either 45 degree angle or square. The latter—shown here—are easier to handle and weld.

Greater penetration power of the electric arc means that preparation of joints by grinding an angle, as with oxyacetylene, is unnecessary.

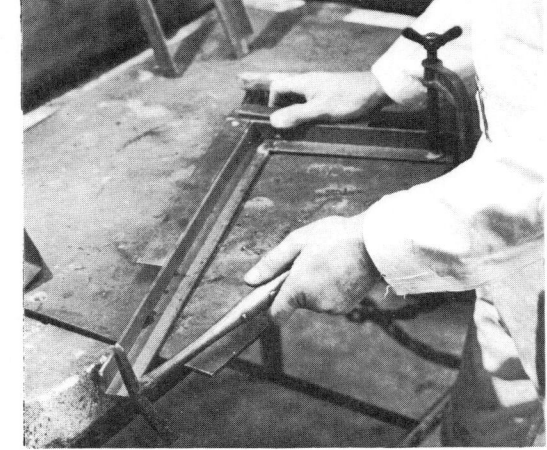

1

2

Clamp one side of the joint to the bench and tack on one side only. Then check with the set square (1) and tack on the other side. Now weld the vertical corner of the joint (2), fixing in an upright position with the clamp. The completed joint here shows one of the points which must be watched in arc welding; there is a deep flaw or 'blowhole' in the weld which will seriously weaken the joint. This must be ground back with a portable grinder before rewelding.

Turn the joint back and reclamp to the table for the main weld (3), taking care to clean the metal before starting. A 4.0 mm electrode using about 150 amps is used to ensure penetration

3

into the joint. A steady, fairly fast action round the angle of the joint (4) will avoid burning the metal.

4

Aim for the sort of weld shown in picture (5), with the slag tapped off. This standard can be attained only with practice.

5

## WELDING JIG

A simple welding jig for ensuring the right-angled joints are welded up squarely comes from Mr. I. A. Brown, Silklands, Buckland Brewer, Bideford, Devon. It consists of two pieces of 38 mm x 38 mm box section 450 mm long welded to form a 90 degree corner.

When two pieces of metal, either box section or angle iron, have to be welded at right angles, Mr. Brown clamps them to the jig so that his hands are free for welding. He mitres the ends

of angle iron before clamping the joint. The corner of the jig is cut off diagonally so that he can make the inside vertical weld while the work is on the jig. When the outside vertical weld and main weld are done, he removes the work from the jig and completes the main internal weld.

For box section joints Mr. Brown clamps work in the same way as for the angle iron, but completes the weld before removal from the square.

Apart from the obvious advantage of lining up the joint quickly, the job can be left to cool on the jig and cannot be pulled out of square as usually happens when free-hand welding cools down and distorts due to contraction.

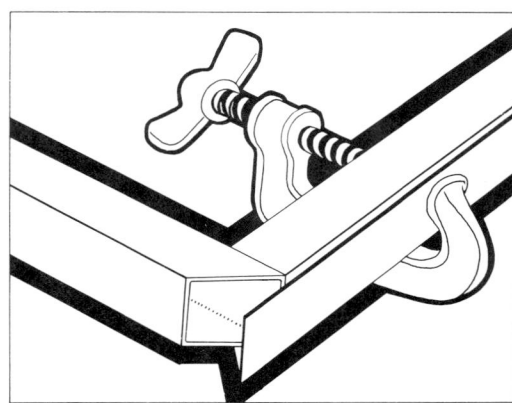

## SLEEVE WELDING

Where lateral strengthening is needed in structural work such as cattle pens or farm gates the joints can be welded with a rod or tube insert fitted. But for crop sprayer booms and other liquid carrying pipe work the flow must not be restricted by weld penetration or insert supports.

Sleeving combines lateral strengthening with an effective repair. Where pipes have been fractured and the broken ends cut off, a sleeve will bridge the gap without shortening the pipe.

Welders with marginal experience will appreciate that a strong watertight joint in two pipes of equal diameter can be difficult to achieve.

In a fractured steel water pipe the first job is to saw off the broken ends and file them smooth. If the work has been dismantled it should first be measured so that it can be spaced in the sleeve to its original specification.

Cut a piece of tube to fit the pipe snugly and to a length that allows two or three inches of overlap on each side. Tack in position with a spot of weld if there is any difficulty in supporting it for welding. Weld in a vertical position as this will make easier the continuous weld that is essential for good work. The weld should be built up to overlap by 6-12 mm to ensure a good watertight weld. Gas or electric arc welding can be used for this type of work.

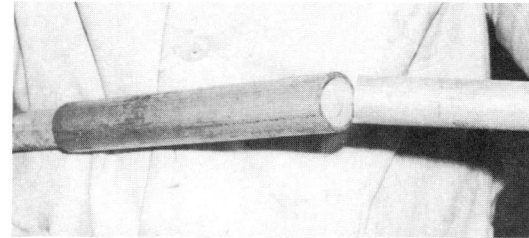

Cut a sleeve to make a close fit over the pipe and overlap the break by 50 to 75 mm.

The arc process is used here with a 2.6 mm general purpose type mild steel electrode and the current set at 30 amps.

A small overlap of weld will help to seal the join. The pipes used in this case were 25 mm galvanised steel water pipe sleeved with similar 30 mm diameter pipe.

## BRONZE WELDING

Bronze welding is quite different from the fusion welding process, though the same basic equipment is used. The bronze rod is melted on the hot metal and flows into the small pores of the metal by capillary action to give a strong bond between parent metal and rod deposit.

Its main advantage is the low temperature—about 850 degrees C—at which it is carried out instead of 1,200 degrees C plus for ordinary fusion welding. The low heat input into the parent metal gives less distortion than ordinary welding and is useful in joining thin sheet metal.

Bronze welding can be used to join dissimilar metals, such as copper and steel, which cannot be fusion welded because of the wide difference in their melting points. Repair of malleable castings is best done with bronze welding, as fusion welding's high temperature will destroy the properties of the casting.

A borax-based flux is used in bronze welding. This cleans the surface of the metal to enable good bonding of the bronze on to the parent metal and helps float off impurities. Special flux-coated rods can be obtained but are expensive.

Flux can be applied by dipping the rod into the flux (1) or it can be mixed into a paste with water and brushed on to the joint before welding commences.

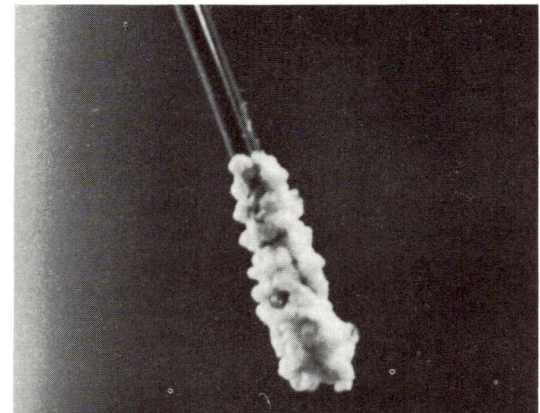

1

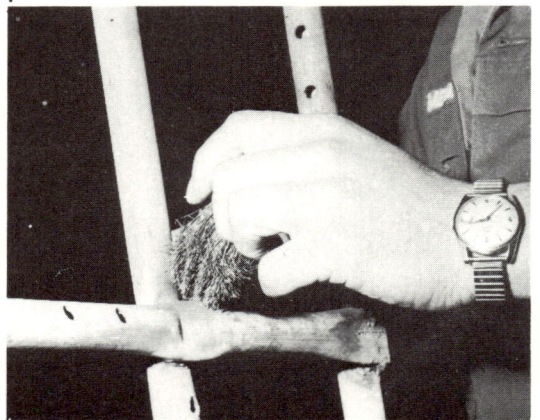

2

Rods most commonly used are nickel bronze for high strength joints or dissimilar metals, manganese bronze for malleable castings and grey cast-iron, and silicon bronze for mild steel or galvanised materials.

Use an oxidising flame to prevent the zinc being boiled away. Insufficient oxygen gives a porous weld. Cleanliness of the joint (2) is essential for a good bond to be formed between the bronze and the parent metal. Clean off all grease, paint and rust and roughen the surface of the metal with a file before welding. Remove all burrs and sharp edges or they will overheat and spoil the weld.

In the example shown 25 mm diameter galvanised pipe is being bronze welded using 3 mm diameter silicon bronze rod. Gas pressures are 0.15 bar for both bottles and a size 7 nozzle is used. Heat the metal to dull red and apply the rod, which should melt if the parent metal is at the correct temperature and leave a deposit which can be built up to the required size (3) (see next page). Avoid overheating the parent metal or the tinning action of the flux is spoilt and the rod deposits run into beads.

The finished job should have a smooth deposit, free from air-holes (4) (see next page).

Zinc fumes are poisonous, so carry out bronze welding in a well-ventilated area.

3    4

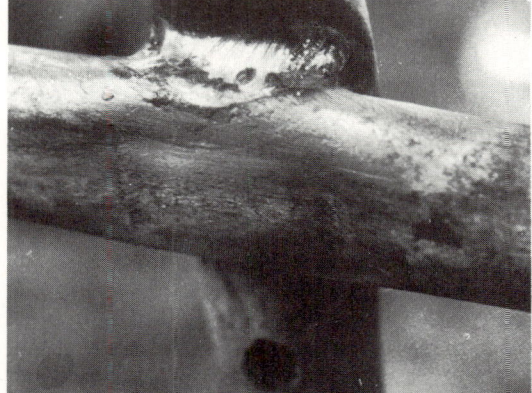

## ROD WELDING

Welding together mild steel rods for shafting or construction work is a fairly straightforward job for the average farm workshop operator. It is also the type of work that can have a number of applications on the farm and a knowledge of the correct procedure will help to avoid the poor or unsightly work that can result from lack of attention to detail.

The oxy-acetylene method is illustrated here using 2 and 3 mm diameter rods respectively with No. 7 and No. 10 nozzles. The oxygen pressure should be set at 0.35 bar, the acetylene at 0.15 bar and the flame adjusted until it is neutral.

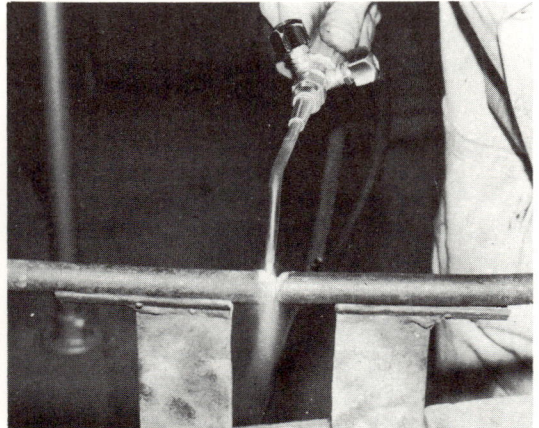

Pictures by courtesy of Rycote Wood College, Thame.

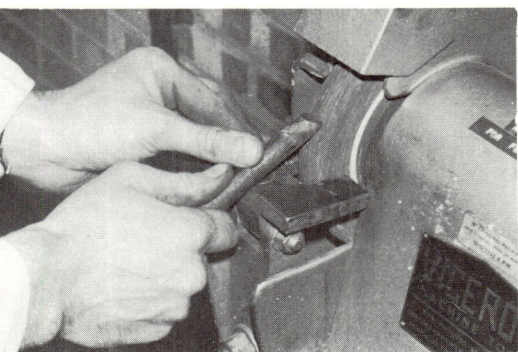

The ends of the two sections of 16 mm diameter mild steel are prepared so that they are bevelled to a double vee at an angle of 45 to 60 deg. Wear on the grinding wheel will be reduced if the outline is first cut with a hacksaw.

The two ends are placed on the weld table with a gap between them of 1.5 to 3.0 mm. The work is heated until it is thoroughly molten before using the 1.5 mm filler rod to complete a run as if welding plate, i.e. with good penetration. The work is then turned over and the run built up—it is essential that a good bone is achieved at this stage.

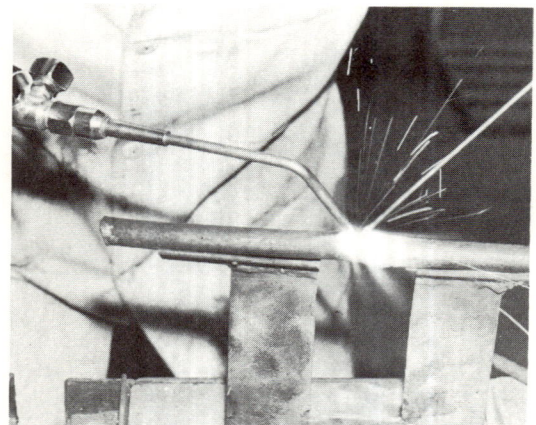

Still on the reverse side continue to build up the join using the 3 mm rod. Do not weld one run on each side alternately or flakey slag will develop and hamper proper work. When this is completed the build-up continues on the other side finishing with a few runs lengthways across the join to leave a good build-up of weld material.

At today's prices and replacement costs, hardsurfacing of wearing metal parts in machinery is obviously useful but the techniques were difficult in the past. There are now two new techniques which make hardsurfacing easier, more accurate and cheaper.

### SPRAY WELDING

It is worth taking a look at spray welding. This is not an entirely new technique but modern equipment has improved it significantly. The idea is to use a specially designed gas welding torch to spray metallic powder on to the surface of a metal part where the flame produces a fused hard surface. A conventional torch with provision to add a can of metallic powder on the top of it and a trigger to release a flow of powder into the flame can be used. The powder sprayed on to the surface of the workpiece is melted by the flame and fuses with the component material. It is a very useful process for surface hardening of cultivator points, plough share, discs and so on. It can also be used for building up worn parts. The spray deposit can be machined so that, with the choice of suitable powder, the technique can be used for building up

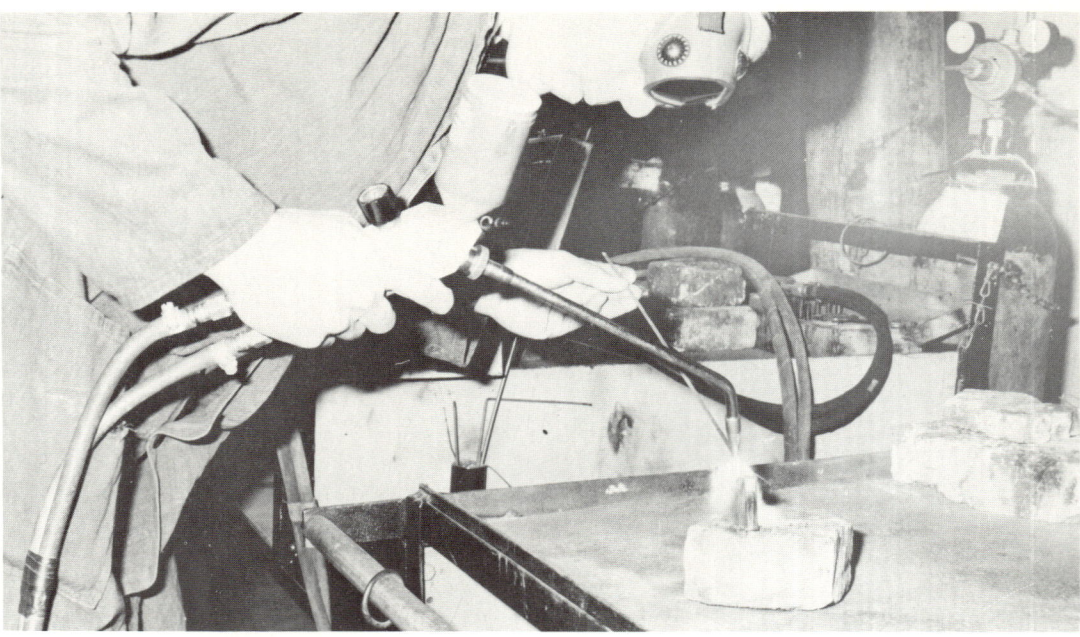

Spray welding showing the gun with powder cannister.

worn shafts which can be turned on a lathe back to the original design size.

One of the major advantages of the technique is that it is very easy to operate. Even people who have not welded before can learn the basics in about ten minutes. The normal welder of average ability will be able to produce good deposits almost immediately and be able to control the evenness and thickness of the added layer. The whole operation is much easier and faster than hardsurfacing by conventional methods of gas or arc welding.

For spray welding, you need really clean, shiny metal parts. New parts, such as cultivator tines for hard surfacing, should be used for a hectare or so before spray surfacing so that the metal is scoured. De-greasing of clean parts with a steam cleaner is good practice. Even finger-marks are best kept off the clean surface and spray welding should be carried out as soon as possible after cleaning, before surface rusting occurs.

The tip of the welding pistol should be held 15 cm or so from the work. The hard surfacing is best applied in thin layers of about 0.254 mm to build up an 'overlay' of powder material on the metal to be surfaced. Several layers can be applied to build up a thicker layer. Attention should be paid to getting an even deposit. After application of the overlay, the temperature of the metal is raised with the welding torch only to a dull red heat. As the overlay melts and fuses to the workpiece surface it will develop a shiny, mirrored surface,

Sweat-on paste being used with a standard gas torch.

and this glazed pool can be drawn along the metal, taking care not to over-heat.

The spray-welding torch will cost in the region of £100, possibly a bit more. It can be used for ordinary welding. The powders will cost about £10 per kg, which would cover about 1,500 sq cm at 1 mm thick.

Alternatively, there is a process that does not need the special pistol for applying powders. You could save the £100 on the kit. The process uses an ordinary torch and a special paste which is 'sweated' on to the metal.

Wall Colmonoy Ltd (of Pontadawe, Glamorgan, Wales, UK.) have developed sweat-on paste for hard surfacing. It is based on chromium boride crystals which are, in the company's words, 'second only to diamonds on the hardness scale and the most abrasion resistant material available for hard surfacing'.

There are three ways to apply sweat-on paste. The gas welding technique is recommended for thin metal sections, the carbon arc method for thicker sections, and the gas tungsten arc technique for smoother, less diluted deposits.

## GAS WELDING

This method, employing an oxyacetylene torch, is ideal for metal thicknesses up to 1.5 mm, and is also very useful for plough shares, harrow discs, cutters and similar farm implements, coal cutter bits or excavator teeth.

To begin, the area to be hard surfaced must be

clean and freed of scale or rust, by grinding if necessary. Paste must be mixed thoroughly, *adding water if necessary,* to bring it to a brushing consistency.

Apply a thin overlay of paste, approximately 2 to 3 mm, to the surface with a fine bristle brush to provide complete coverage. *Allow to dry.* Then, using a reducing flame with feather equal to the length of a cone (a 2X flame), begin fusing the paste to the base metal with an oxyacetylene torch. Heat should first be applied to the bare base metal adjacent to the overlay of paste. When this metal becomes red, apply the flame to the paste surface until the paste sweats into the surface of the steel. Sweating is indicated by the quenching of the bright colour as it bonds to the base metal. Heating should progress as fast as the sweating to prevent puddling of the steel surface.

Carbon arc welding, and gas tungsten arc equipment is not normally available on the farm but it is preferred for heavier work. It would be better for heavier earth engaging parts such as plough shares or chisel points but the use of normal gas welding equipment is ideal for thinner components such as discs and can give good results on the thicker and heavier parts. The paste is £12.50 to £15.00 per kg and may make parts last several times as long.

## TAKING CARE OF GAS WELDING NOZZLES

Gas welding tips and nozzles should be stored in a rack or clean box to prevent the gas hole from becoming blocked by dirt. When fitting a nozzle to the torch use the correct spanner. Pliers will damage the flats on the nut. Tighten the nozzle just enough to provide a gas-tight joint.

Over a period the gas hole will become misshapen due to heat from the metal being welded, blowbacks, metal spitting back through overheating, or the nozzle touching the molten welding pool. An odd flame shape difficult to control will form and give an uneven weld.

Clean the tip by using a fine file until the tip is square and smooth. To reshape the hole use a set of nozzle reamers. These are sold in sets of **14**, which will cover most standard nozzle sizes. Each reamer is made of hardened metal with fine cutting teeth on the shank.

First use a reamer a size smaller than the nozzle size, working it in and out of the hole, removing the burrs and carbon particles. Do not overdo it or you will have an oversize hole that will not deliver the proper volume of gas at the set pressure and will not function properly. Then change to the recommended size of reamer and repeat the operation. If no reamers are available a small drill will do for the larger-sized nozzles, but do not twist it or it will cut the soft copper and enlarge the hole (see picture next page).

A worn welding nozzle with a poorly-shaped gas hole, is shown alongside three normal nozzles.

File the nozzle end until perfectly flat.

The final operation is to ream out the hole

Light up after cleaning and check flame shape. Welding flames should be smooth and straight. Pre-heat flames on cutting nozzles should be of equal size and straight, with the oxygen jet evenly shaped and smooth.

Carbon deposits inside the nozzles and shanks can be removed with a powder from the manufacturers of the welding equipment. Dissolve a small amount of powder in water and soak the nozzles for 24 hours to loosen the carbon particles. Dry off the nozzles and blow them out with an airline to remove all the bits.

On heavy work, where a large nozzle producing a lot of heat is used, the nozzle and shank will get hot from reflected heat. To prevent overheating plunge the torch into cold water occasionally during work. Shut off the acetylene, but leave a small volume of oxygen flowing to prevent water entering the torch valves.

Welding nozzle rack

## WELDING NOZZLE RACK

Store welding nozzles and spanners on the wall by the welding bay, or where the welding equipment is kept. This easily-made rack for nozzles consists of a batten of wood with holes drilled for each size nozzle and the number painted by the appropriate hole.

For a spanner rack, paint the outline of each spanner on a length of wood and knock in nails to hold each one in place. You can then see at a glance if a spanner is missing or in the wrong place.

## A JOB USING ARC WELDING

Suppose one end of the yoke on a M-F tractor radius rod snaps off after collision. A new arm will cost several pounds, but a welding repair, just as strong, takes only an hour.

First prepare the broken ends for welding. The metal is about **10 mm** thick so use a double-vee preparation to ensure good fusion of the two parts throughout the whole thickness of metal.

Angle the broken edges at 45—60 degrees on a grinding wheel. Do not take any more metal off than is necessary or a big gap will be left between the two parts that will be difficult to fill with weld deposit.

Next task is to set the parts in their correct position so that when rewelded the job is as near specification as possible. It must be lined up two ways. First, the holes must be in line with each other, and secondly the distance between the two arms must be the same as before.

Clamp the arm in a vice and use spacers and washers, and a length of bar through the yoke eyes, to line up the arms. Clamp the job rigid with G clamps.

For an arm made of medium carbon steel ideally a nickel and steel alloy electrode with low heat input should be used to minimise distortion.

Clean the break, clamp the arm the line up the arms and the holes.

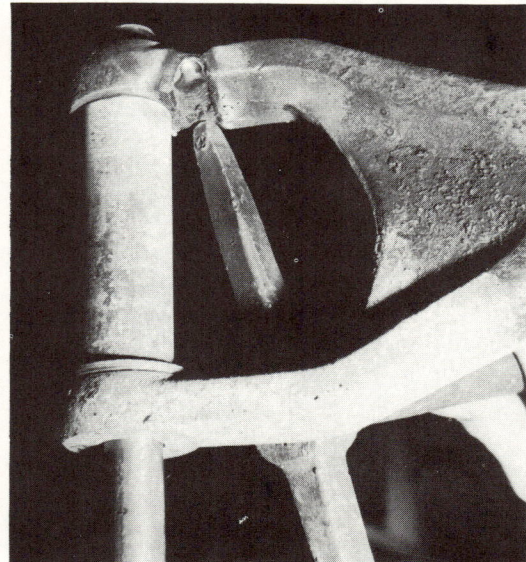

Check progress after each run, and chip away slag.

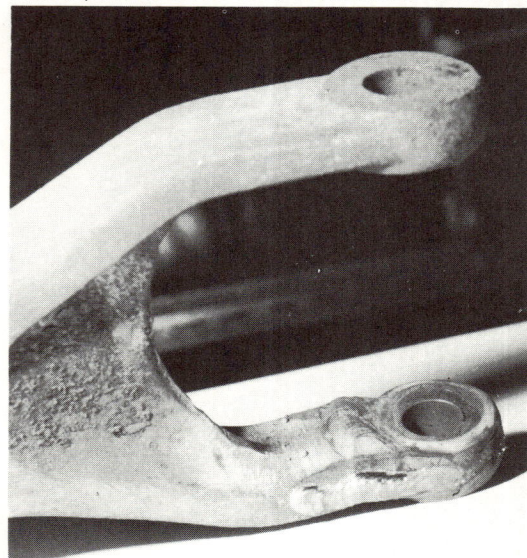

Add a bead along both sides of the weld for added strength.

It leaves a malleable deposit that work-hardens, but the electrode is expensive.

A cheaper alternative is mild steel electrode 3.2 mm at 90 amps. Three runs might be needed on each side of the vee. Check after each run that the job is still true as the welding heat may pull the parts out of true. To give extra strength to the job, lay a bead along the edge of each side of the yoke. After welding, peen the weld with a hammer to relieve any stresses that have built up.

## WELDING THICK METAL

There is no need for special preparation when welding material up to 5 mm thick, except to remove any rust and to leave a narrow gap between the two pieces to be welded to ensure adequate penetration.

Where material is more than 6 or 7 mm thick electric arc welding is generally used for speed and ease, and the material must be 'veed' out to an angle of 45—60 degrees before welding commences. 'Veeing' gives good penetration of the arc and allows the metal to be fused throughout its thickness, thus giving a strong joint.

Single vee preparation is used on materials 5 to 10 mm thick where it is difficult to get at the underside of the weld. It requires more rods to fill the vee, is more expensive, and causes greater distortion. Use double vee preparation if it is possible to reach both sides of the weld. Double vee takes longer to prepare but saves electrodes and minimises distortion by laying a run on alternate sides, each bead counteracting the distortion of its predecessor. The best way to make the vee is to use an oxy-acetylene cutter and a piece of angle iron. Lay the angle iron on its two edges near the metal edge to be prepared. Lay the nozzle parallel to the side of the angle iron and cut off the unwanted metal at a 45 degree angle set by the side of the angle iron. You should get a good enough finish to the metal without further

A length of angle iron helps ensure that the cut is straight and at the correct angle for welding. Clean up rough edges on a grindstone.

preparation, but if necessary clean up the cut on the grindstone and remove slag.

Other methods of forming the vee are by portable grinder, hammer and chisel, or filing though these are much slower.

To weld the pieces together use the largest electrode possible for speed and to minimise distortion, but make sure you do not overheat the metal. First weld the two root runs in the bottom of the vee. Next lay a run slightly to one side of the vee to build up the gap. The next run will be

After laying the first bead, turn the job over and check that weld metal has penetrated right through the vee. Here the pointer indicates good penetration, but there are portions where there is little penetration.

on the other face of the vee and so on, until the weld is up to the level of the parent metal. Take care to remove all the slag for each run, to prevent porosity and poor welds. The last run on the top of the metal should be done with a weave to give a good finish to the weld and strength and reinforcement to the joint.

In the example shown, using 12 mm thick material, the root runs were carried out with 3.2 mm rods at 120 amps setting and the other runs with a 4 mm rod at about 145 amps.

After the root runs lay beads on alternate sides of the joint so minimising distortion. The second and third runs are laid on opposite sides of the vee faces and the fourth one along the top to give a level finish.

## KEEPING CAST IRON WELDING CLEAN

Cast iron is one of the most commonly-used metals in agricultural machinery. It is cheap to produce, hard wearing and has a long life. Its drawback is that unless it is malleable cast iron, it is brittle and easily broken.

Preheating and postheating should take place at the chalk marks on the sprocket rim to prevent cracking as the metal expands and contracts due to the heat of the welding process. Note the fire bricks round the sprocket to prevent draughts which will cause uneven heating and cooling.

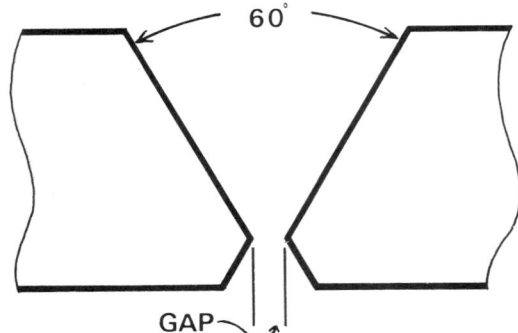

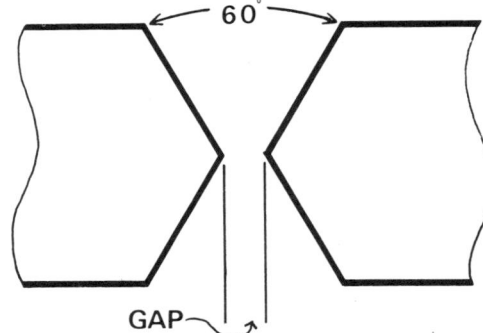

The left-hand diagram shows a typical single-vee preparation and on the right a double-vee preparation. The gap between the two pieces of metal will vary but a rough guide is about 2 to 3 mm.

The sprocket in the pictures was from a combine and was broken by a hammer used to remove it. Fusion welding was used to repair the broken part, though bronze welding could equally well have been used.

The two main points of the job are cleanliness and pre-heating of the sprocket before welding and post-heating after welding.

All grease and dirt should be removed with a proprietary degreasing compound. If petrol or paraffin are used make sure the sprocket is dry before welding. Removing dirt cannot be over-emphasised. Carbon from oil or grease can cause gas bubbles in the weld giving a weak porous joint.

Pre-heating to a dull red heat (550—660 degrees C) prevents stresses in the casting either before or after welding. These stresses can cause cracking in other parts of the casting or distortion. Post-heating ensures that the weld cools slowly and a strong machineable deposit is made. Rapid cooling will leave a hard brittle white iron deposit that is difficult to machine.

In the job shown 4.5 mm square rods containing enough silicon to leave a machinable deposit were used.

Welding the metal. Heat the part to be welded until it is plastic. Test for this with rod using a stirring motion to melt the rod in the molten pool of the parent metal. Two runs were used here, one a root run in the bottom of the vee and a filing run to give a level surface.

Preparing the crack. A spatula made out of ordinary mild steel welding rod is used to scrape molten metal away from the crack. A 90 degree vee should be formed to about half the thickness of the casting.

After both sides have been welded clean off the slag with a wire brush, and paint it while still warm. Check when the sprocket is refitted to the machine that it runs true.

A No 5 nozzle was used to weld, and both gas bottles were set at 0.2 bar.

A cast iron flux containing slag-producing compounds was used to dissolve oxides of iron and protect the metal from oxidation during welding.

One side of the spoke was prepared and welded and the process was repeated on the other side. Total time taken was about one hour and the combine went back to work instead of waiting for a spare from the factory.

### SPARK LIGHTER

An old magneto mounted on a plate fitted with a set of contact points—gap about 3 mm—or a spark plug is useful for lighting a welding torch. Flick the drive coupling to produce a spark. Weld it to the bottle frame and it is always available for use.

# METAL CUTTING WITH OXY-ACETYLENE

As well as being an extremely useful tool for repair jobs and fabricating equipment, your oxy-acetylene welding kit can also be used for fast, moderately-accurate cutting-out of sheet and bar steel. For an additional outlay of about £25 for a Sapphire cutting head you can tackle most of the cutting jobs likely to occur in the farm workshop.

For these jobs your standard regulator gauges are quite adequate, although for very heavy cutting—metal greater than 12 mm thick—you will need an additional high-pressure gauge set.

The cutting head (1) screws on to the hand-grip base of the normal welding torch and consists of the special right-angled head, the tube arrangement to provide large quantities of oxygen—which produces the great heat needed to burn through metal—and the special, thumb-grip oxygen control.

With the cutter you should have a set of cutting nozzles for different metal thicknesses. These are made in sizes from 1 mm, in 2 mm stages upwards. A set of three nozzles from 2 mm to 8 mm will cut everything from 6 mm sheet to 25 mm bar. These will cost about £4 each.

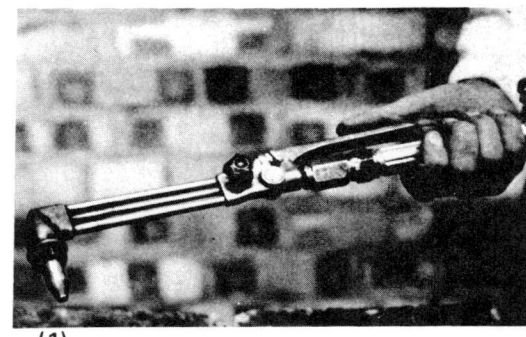

(1)

(2)

(3)

(4)

(5)

As with welding, some practice will be needed before you can cut accurately, particularly on curved work. Before starting, mark out the metal (2) with a chalk line and centre-punch along it. The chalk will disappear as soon as the flame touches it.

Next set the flame. Light up as for normal welding and, using the valves on the torch (3)— do not touch the thumb valve at this stage—adjust for a normal, neutral flame with an equal balance of acetylene and oxygen.

The only setting difference on the bottle gauges is that the oxygen pressure will be much higher—1.7 bar for cutting 6 mm metal and 2.1 bar for 12 mm.

The metal to be cut should be held steady by weights or a vice and the body of the torch should be steadied on the fingers of the left hand resting on the bench. Make a swift practice run across the line of the cut, with a little pressure on the excess oxygen thumb-valve to clean the metal then start to cut (4).

The nozzle must be vertical and the point of the flame 3 mm above the metal. Heat at the edge until the metal is bright red, then switch on the excess oxygen to set fire to the metal. Draw the torch steadily towards you until the job is completed. Where a series of pieces of metal of a similar length or width are being cut, a guide fitted to the nozzle base (5) will speed up work considerably.

Another ancillary use for the welding kit is for metal heating—particularly useful for in situ forging jobs (6). A simple, straight-heating torch is screwed on to the handgrip and, with gauge pressures set at 0.15 to 0.2 bar both acetylene and

(6)

oxygen, a slightly carburising flame—with more acetylene than oxygen—is set to give concentrated, steady heat wherever it is needed.

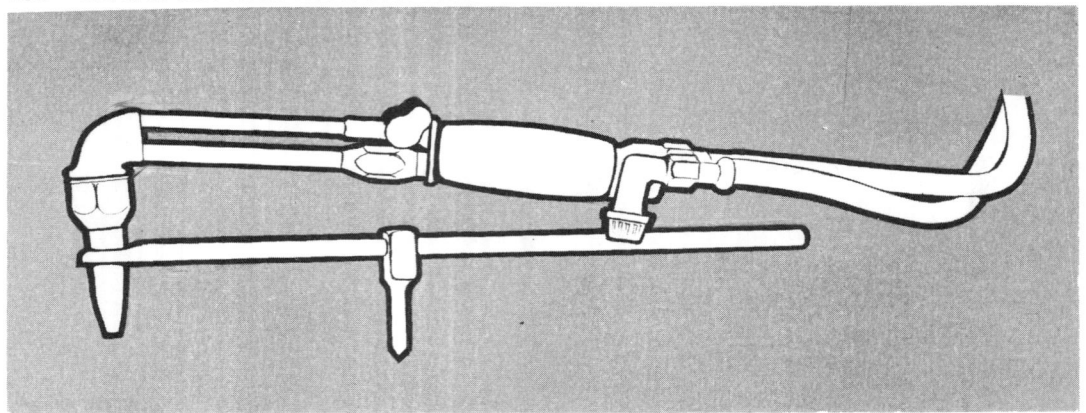

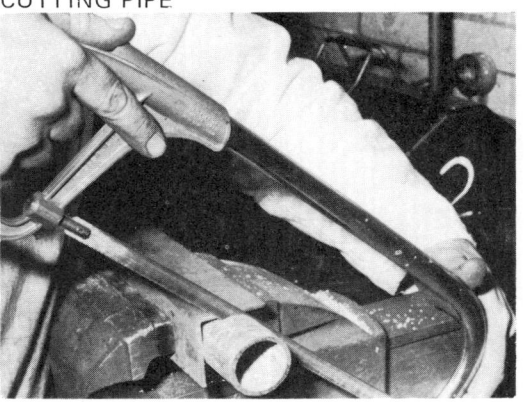

## BETTER CURVES FROM THE CUTTING TORCH

Cutting large holes, circular discs or even curved shapes from mild steel is made easier by a simple jig to hold the cutting nozzle and control its movement to the desired radius.

The one illustrated was made in a few minutes by Mr. J. R. Marshall, Chapel Lane, Nettleham, Lincoln, from a length of 10 mm diameter bar to form a radius piece, with a small square of 6 mm plate welded to the end.

Drill a hole in the plate big enough to take the cutting nozzle on the large end of the taper. A short length of 12 mm bar, drilled through to take the radius piece and on one side to take, after drilling and tapping, a 6 mm diameter stud with a wing-nut attached, forms the body of the pivot point. Weld a short-pointed peg in the bottom of the block to form the pivot.

Since cutting nozzles very in external diameter and length, the size of the hole in which the nozzle fits and the length of the pivot peg (which will control the height of the nozzle tip above the metal) must be made to fit the actual torch with which the jig is to be used.

A little practice with the jig will enable quite acceptable curved cuts to be made, as long as the basic rule that the cut is always started in the waste metal is observed.

Cutting a thread on a pipe can be difficult unless the end of the pipe is hacksawed off squarely.

A simple way to ensure a square cut is to use a piece of angle iron with the flanges cut square to each other. Lay the pipe in the angle iron, with the square end of the angle iron on the mark where the pipe is to be cut, and clamp both pipe and angle iron in the vice. Now saw the pipe, using the angle iron as a guide. Keep the blade close to the two flanges and the cut will be square.

If mitred ends are required, such as for gates, simply mark out and cut one flange of the angle iron at 45 deg to the other. Clamping the pipe and angle iron in a vice and cutting along the 45 deg flange will give a close fitting joint for welding without further preparation.

# SPRAYING AND SPRAYERS

The success or failure of chemical sprays depends on how expertly they are applied. As little as 5 grams of chemical may have to be placed evenly over one hectare and to spray without thoroughly inspecting the machine can result in a valuable crop getting a killer dose or none at all.

Calibration is all-important. First check the handbook for the correct nozzle tips for the application rate and the pressure at which they should be worked. Set the engine speed to give, say, 6.5 kmph in the gear to be used—check that this is achieved in practice by measuring the distance travelled in one minute in the field. If the tractor has a speedometer, so much the better and easier.

If you have a tramlining system and are, for example, working a 12 m sprayer behind 3 runs of a 4 m drill, then the calibration of the sprayer is worked out like this:

There are 10,000 sq metres in a hectare and 6.5 kmph is 6,500 m/hr. So, for a 12 m sprayer to cover one hectare, it will take:

$$\frac{10,000 \times 60}{6,500 \times 12} = 7.69 \text{ minutes}$$

Fill up the sprayer tank, run it for 7.69 minutes (i.e. 7 min 41 sec) and measure how many litres are required to refill the tank but remember that the tractor engine speed must be the same as that required to run the tractor at the chosen ground speed in the field (i.e. in this example, at 6.5 kmph).

To find the amount of spray that would be applied to one hectare measure the amount of water required to refill the tank.

Method is as important as the measure. Spray twice round the outside of the field to give a good headland and where possible spray the remainder, following the drills. Better still, replan your operation as soon as possible to run on a tramline system. If this is not feasible yet, take some care in marking out.

Tie a length of cord 2 m longer than the boom to each end so that when turning at the headland the free end of the cord will stay in position until the turn is completed, making it easy to match up the next run.

Watch for blocked nozzles and steer a straight course. If a nozzle becomes blocked do not stop in mid-field, otherwise the drips from the nozzles may damage the crop. Stop the sprayer and, using the previous wheel marks, drive to the headland. Reverse into the hedge bottom and put on a set of clean tips.

Wash and clean the sprayer at the end of each day's work, bearing in mind that it may be a week or so before it is next used.

Don't forget the pump just because it is hidden under the tank. Clean and lightly lubricate the drive coupling and make sure it can be turned freely by hand before coupling on the top shaft. Inspect the hoses, keep the face-bolts tight and make sure the securing chain is fixed.

Wash out the tank to remove any scale form-

Inspect the filters for breaks in the gauze.

ed during storage, especially under the tank top. Inspect the filters for breaks in the gauze and repair minor splits with solder. Filter inserts should be changed according to the manual and a check on the jubilee clips with a screwdriver is useful.

## NOZZLE CARE

Remove all the nozzles, filters and end caps and wash thoroughly **(1). Pump water through and tap the pipes at the same time to dislodge any foreign matter.**

Clean nozzle filters, but do not over-tighten when re-fitting. It is best to fit new tips to make sure the pattern is right from the outset. When replacing the nozzles keep the pump working and, starting from the centre, work outwards, so that as each nozzle is fitted the pressure in the boom builds up, **flushing out dirt through the ends.** Check that the end caps are a good fit.

Spray water through the nozzles and inspect each one for correct delivery. Even if the slightest streak can be seen, change the tip—remembering that even new tips can be faulty. A simple check is to hold a jam jar under each nozzle for a set period. Unless the nozzles are right the rest can be a waste of time (2).

Some chemicals do not mix easily, so half fill the tank with clean water, start the pump and agitator and then add the chemical. Never put neat chemical in the tank or it will go straight down the pipes and not be mixed. Wash everything used during mixing, top up the tank and stir with a clean stick.

To keep foaming to a minimum, check the suction pipes for air leaks and if the sprayer has a recirculatory agitating system make sure the end of the return pipe is always covered with liquid.

Finally, make sure the pressure gauge is working correctly. **It gets a lot of vibration on a mounted unit and it is advisable to change it every year.**

(2)

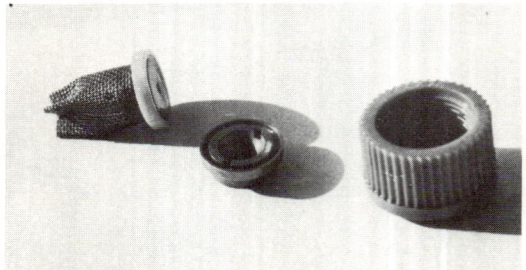

(1)

## OPERATION AND PRECAUTIONS

Having set up the sprayer there are a number of do's and don'ts about using it which must be followed. Not the least of these are adequate safeguards for the driver.

Every year operators are injured through careless handling of chemicals. Some sprays are made more dangerous by their cumulative effect. It is the gradual build-up of poisonous chemicals rather than the immediate effect which does the damage.

The Health and Safety Executive has leaflets which give guidance on regulations and advise on precautions. With some chemicals certain protective clothing must be worn.

The obvious precautions, such as not spraying on windy days, particularly if the wind is blowing towards livestock, or near pastures in use, susceptible crops, gardens or orchards, need an annual reminder. Read the chemical tin label carefully; don't rely on memory. The makers may have changed its shape and colour and the application rate.

Send back the empties without delay if they are returnable. Burn or wash out, puncture and bury the others. Lock up those stored and don't keep them near fertilisers, feed or seed.

Wash the sprayer with detergent—inside and outside—immediately after use. Don't let the washing water seep or drain into domestic or other water supplies.

Operators should wear protective clothing, never try to clear a blocked nozzle by sucking or blowing, and never smoke while working, They should wash well before smoking, eating or drinking, and after work. Keep clear of spray drift and wash maintain protective clothing before storing.

## CHECK-UP ON SPRAYER PUMPS

Three main types of pump—gear, roller vane and diaphragm—are in common use on the farm. All will apply popular chemicals, but if gritty suspensions or liquid fertilisers are to be used in any quantity the following information will be useful.

Gear pumps are fast disappearing from regular use because they wear quickly with suspensions. The pump has two gears, one driving, one driven, contained in a tight-fitting metal casing with inlet and outlet ports. An adjustable relief valve in the circuit prevents overloading and controls delivery pressure.

Liquid is carried round the outside between the gear teeth and the casing and delivered under pressure as the teeth come into mesh.

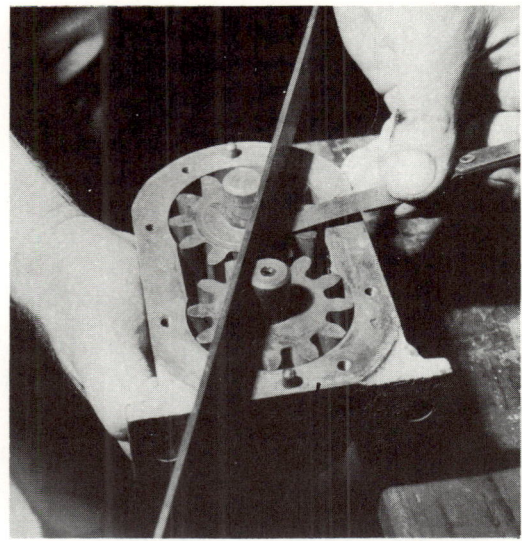

Gear pumps wear rapidly if used with suspension chemicals. Check condition of the gear faces with feeler gauges as shown above.

Gear pumps are suitable for non-suspension chemicals only as grit will rapidly wear teeth, end plates and casing. Gears and housing are made of phosphor bronze and/or steel and the main point to check is wear between gears and end plate. Place a straight edge across the face of the gears and casing and measure the gap between the straight edge and gear faces with a feeler gauge. **Any more than 0.025 to 0.040 mm will allow liquid to escape and the required pressure will not be reached.**

Roller vane pumps are the most popular type at the moment, being fitted to many sprayers. Their main advantages are that relatively high pressures can be reached and they have a long life with proper maintenance. A cast-iron chamber has an offset slotted rotor, and rollers held in the slots roll in and out under centrifugal force,

A roller vane pump should be checked once a year. Replace all the rollers if any are cracked or show signs of ridging.

carrying liquid from inlet to outlet point. Liquid is forced out under pressure as the gap between rotor and housing decreases opposite the delivery port.

Two types of roller are common, a weighted nylon one for non-gritty chemicals and a synthetic rubber or ebonite roller for gritty materials. Carry a spare set of both types of roller and spare sealing gaskets so that it is easy to change from one type of chemical to another.

Watch for wear on the gear pump cover plate. Replace or have it faced if scored.

Inspect the pump once a year for damaged rollers. Worn rollers will be cracked or ridged and will give low pressures. Replace them in sets to maintain the pump's balance.

Diaphragm pumps, although initially more expensive than gear or roller vane pumps, have a long life and need little maintenance. All types of liquid can be applied with them. Most parts in contact with liquid are rubber or plastic, so there is no rust problem.

The pump works like a fuel lift pump in an engine. Main troubles are sticking valves on a holed diaphragm.

Maintenance is a simple matter of lifting the head and fitting a new rubber diaphragm and plastic valves. Most diaphragm pumps are multi-chambered to damp out pulsations inherent in the design.

Always turn roller and gear pumps by hand before fitting to the pto, and prime them before use. Never run them dry or rapid wear will occur. Grease them regularly.

Store gear and roller pumps full of oil. If they are to be left unused for a few days run de-watering fluid through them to prevent rusting. Always tie a pump to some part of the tractor frame to prevent it rotating round the shaft and damaging the hoses (see picture, next page).

Keep all connections tight and when re-assembling make sure all bolts on the face plates are tightened evenly to prevent distortion.

Always tie the pump body to the tractor frame to make sure that t cannot rotate.

Each half of the boom is secured with one nut and a spring.

## CHEAP MARKERS FOR ACCURATE FERTILISING

With fertiliser, spinner spreading widths and spray boom lengths increasing, some form of marker to indicate where the last bout finished is essential.

Mr. John Pope, Cuckmans Farm, Ragged Hall Lane, St. Albans, Herts, made a cheap set of markers from **40 mm diameter tube and 12 mm**

diameter round bar for the **12 m** spread of his fertiliser distributor. He attached the markers to the tractor front weight frame.

Two **6 m** booms are made with the tube and braced, to prevent them bending and bouncing, with struts made from the round bar. The end of the bar that fits into a hole on the angle-iron carrying frame is threaded to take a nut.

Each boom is slid on a prong on the angle-iron framework and the threaded ends of the bars are pushed through two **16 mm** holes in the upright

part of the frame. A nut and old valve spring hold each boom in position and cushion shock loads.

A chain of **1 m** bolted to each end of the boom acts as a marker. To make more easily seen marks, Mr. Pope ties a small coil of barbed wire to the end of the chain.

Fitting the booms is a one-man job. Rest one end of the boom on a short length of wood stuck in the ground while the nut and spring are fastened.

# WINTER STORAGE

## THE BALER

Before winter storing the baler, first clean it inside and out to remove dirt, old grease and crop residue. (1) Dirt left on surfaces over winter gathers moisture, which causes corrosion and in time may cause paint to peel. It is pointless to treat with anti-rust surfaces which are dirty.

Disconnect the pto shaft safety slip clutch from the flywheel and slacken off the spring tension (2).

**1** This tractor exhaust cleaning attachment can be used for applying a protective coating of oil as well as removing dirt.

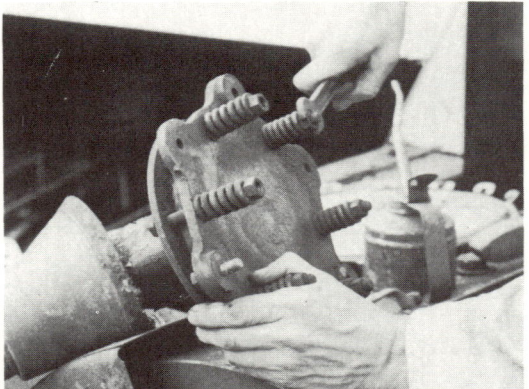

**2** Clutch friction surfaces are best left without any special treatment. Apply oil to the nuts and stud threads.

**3** Grease will prevent the drive flanges seizing together.

Remove the flywheel shear bolt and coat the drive flanges with thick grease (3). Leave the shear bolt out, to prevent children turning the baler and injuring themselves.

Check the pto shaft safety guards and grease the universal couplings, taking care not to pump in too much grease and rupture the dust seals.

Wash down the knotters and remove any strands of twine from the retainers. Clean dirt from the teeth of drive gears (4) and, once the knotter assemblies are clean, coat them with oil or anti-rust, grease all nipples and protect with a waterproof cover.

**4** The knotter disc brake should not be oiled or greased. Either leave it dry or use a special anti-rust solution.

Chains should be cleaned with paraffin and coated with thick grease (5). Some must be removed for treatment and care must be taken when refitting to see that the timing is correct. Another way of treating chains is to boil them for half-an-hour in transmission oil or tallow.

This allows the lubricant to penetrate into the pins and bushes.

Clear any crop which has become wound round the pick-up tine bars and clean the drive cam (6). Coat with anti-rust the stripper loops and all other areas where paint has worn off.

To treat the bale chamber, first unscrew the bale density adjusting cranks and oil the adjuster screw threads (7). Pull out the last couple of bales. If these are left over the winter they will gather moisture, expand and could buckle the sides of the chamber. Coat the inside of the cham-

**5** Soak chain in paraffin for half an hour then brush off old grease and dirt.

**6** Removing the end stripper loops allows easy access to the pick-up drive cam.

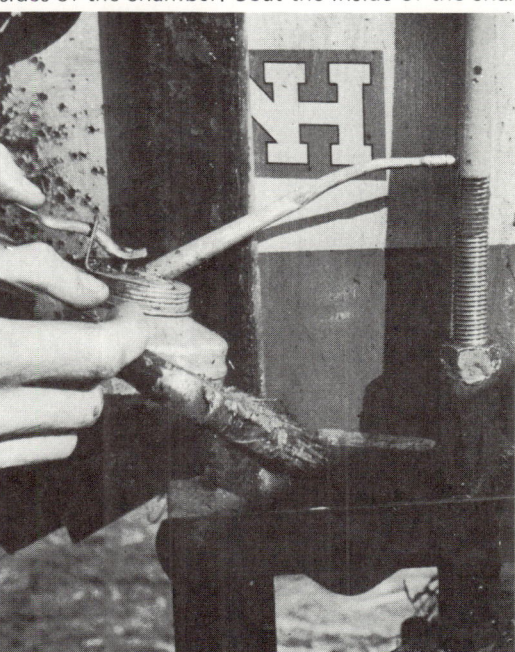

**7** An old paint brush makes an ideal oil applicator and ensures that the whole area is covered.

ber with oil and cover the plunger guide rails with thick grease (8). Soaking straw with waste oil and feeding it through the baler makes this job easier.

Remove both shear knives, resharpen, coat with grease and store in a dry place (9).

Rub down and repaint all chipped or scratched surfaces, using a red oxide primer and an enamel topcoat.

Jack up the baler on blocks.

**8** After applying grease to the plunger guide rails, turn the bales over a couple of times to distribute it.

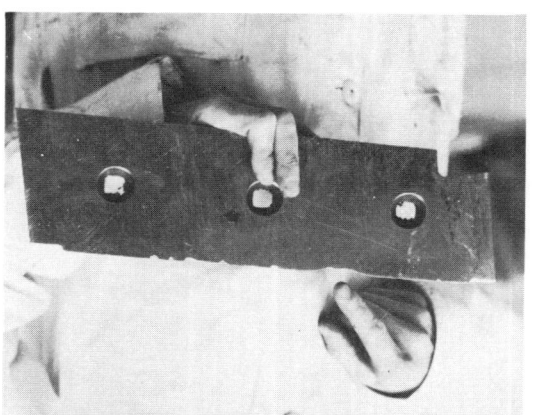

**9** Knife edges may be built up with weld and reground to shape. This is a job for a qualified welder, special welding rods and technique are necessary.

**10** Coat twine tension plates and guides with grease.

## THE COMBINE

Preparing a combine for winter storage is as important as daily maintenance during harvest. A quick rub down, draining the radiator and throwing a sack over the engine are not enough if trouble-free operation is expected next year.

Cleaning, inside and outside, is best done before the muck and dust hardens. Compressed air is the best method, but stubborn dirt may require water or paraffin. Grain and chaff in the elevators and grain pans attract vermin, which look upon rubber seals, canvas flaps and elevator flights as part of their diet. However clean the combine, rats and mice will make it their winter home. Leave inspection doors and covers open so that

Example of rubbish accumulation in a neglected machine.

(Left) Remove sieves, wire brush the louvres and lubricate the pivot points.

(Right) Clean the knife thoroughly and coat it with anti-rust. Apply it while the knife is still supported in the cutterbar.

Clean out the stone traps and concave.

they may run freely through the machine; if they become trapped they will eat through the first piece of rubber or canvas they come to.

Running the combine at full blast for a few minutes will get rid of most dirt and dust. Grain in the tank and grain pans may be removed by stuffing a handful of straw into the augers. As the straw is carried along it takes the loose grain with it.

To prevent rust inside soak straw with waste oil, feed it through the drum at a fairly fast rate and run the engine at full throttle. Do this two or three times if necessary.

Check nuts and bolts for tightness and grease each bearing, remembering to pump out the old grease. Make a note of unsolved troubles experienced during the season and list worn parts, so that they may be ordered ready for the yearly overhaul.

Next comes the cutter bar and platform. Remove crop residue and apply a coating of rust preventative to polished surfaces, taking particular care with the cutter bar fingers. Take off the lifter tines and store them in the workshop.

Remove the knife and check it for broken sections. Check the retractable fingers in the feed auger and coat them with anti-rust. Clean

off the platform skids and paint the surface with waste oil. Make sure the whole platform is on to a level surface, otherwise it will become distorted.

Slacken the reel drive safety clutch and other friction drive clutches to prevent the discs sticking to the drive plates.

Flat belts should, as a rule, be left in tension to stop them shrinking and twisting, but V belts should be removed or slackened.

For machines with hydraulically-operated speed variator pulleys on the drum and transmission drives the belt tension may be released by starting the engine, moving appropriate to the fastest speed, then stopping the engines and releasing the pressure on the pulley flanges by levering them apart.

The polished parts of all pulleys should be given a coat of anti-rust: keep it off belt surfaces.

Remove chains where possible, wash thoroughly in paraffin and leave in an oil bath. Chains which cannot be removed may be sprayed with a protective compound available in aerosols.

Clean out both cross augers and elevators. Leave the inspection doors off.

Release tension on platform lift ram assisting springs and coat the uncovered section of the piston rods with anti-rust.

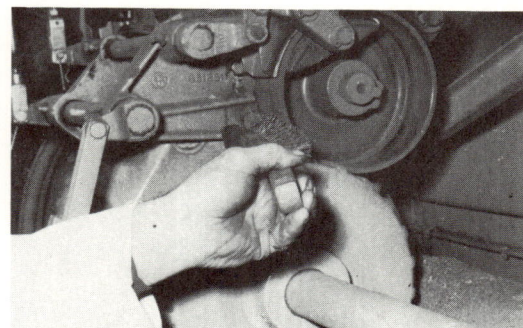

Wire brush the transmission brake drum and coat with anti-rust. Leave the brake lever in the off position.

Retract all hydraulic rams or coat the uncovered sections of the piston rod with thick heavy grease. The rams and shaft splines in the speed variator pulleys should also be treated. Care must be taken not to get grease on the belts.

External brake drums and discs should be cleaned and coated with anti-rust.

Jack up the wheels and reduce the tyre pressure to **about 0.7 bar. Release the brakes and fix the clutch pedal in the disengaged position to prevent sticking** and seizing during the winter.

Check the paintwork and touch up damaged areas.

Scrape the inside of the straw walker with a length of pipe.

Grease the splines of the pulley drive shaft after levering the flanges apart.

Remove straw which has accumulated in the fan housing.

Variable speed pulleys should be given special attention to prevent corrosion of the highly polished flanges.

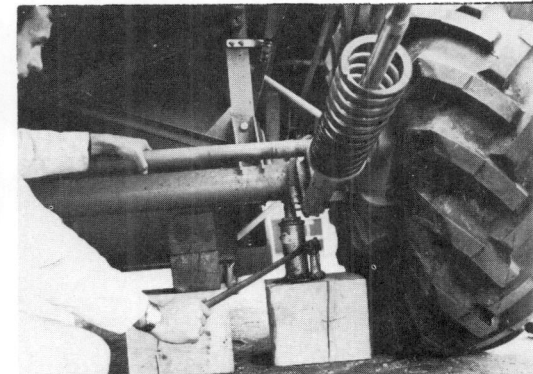

Jack the wheels clear of the ground and support on blocks. Cover the tyres and reduce the pressure to **about 0.7 bar.**

Run the engine until it reaches normal operating temperature, then change the oil and oil filter.

Clean the air filter and change the oil. Run the engine for about 15 minutes and, while still running, squirt upper cylinder lubricant into the air intake manifold. Stop the engine while it is exhausting black smoke.

Seal air intake pipes, crankcase breather, exhaust pipe and oil filler with waterproof material (polythene bags are ideal). Cover the dynamo and control box.

Drain the radiator and put the filler cap on the driver's seat as a warning.

Top up the fuel tank to prevent the build-up of condensation and seal the filler cap.

Remove the battery, keep it topped up and charged; if possible, use it on another vehicle for a few days every two months.

Dirt on the battery terminals tends to collect moisture. This can cause a direct short between two cells.

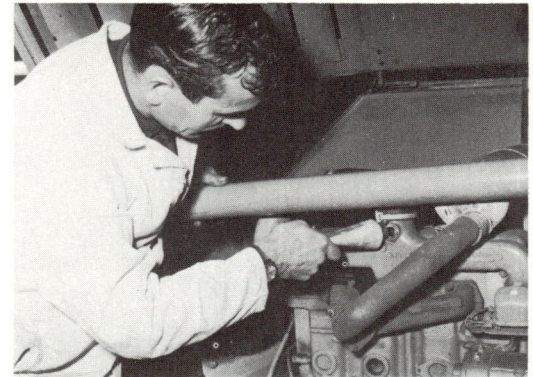

An old washing-up detergent container makes an excellent oil can.

An example of frost damage to a cylinder head.

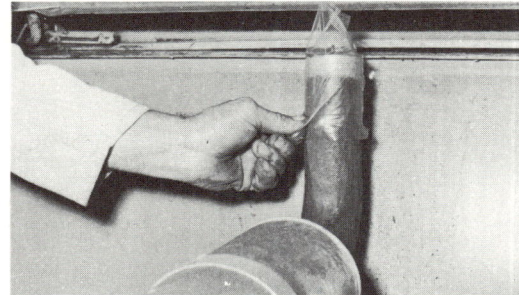

Seal the exhaust pipe and all air intake pipes.

## FOLDING A 'V' BELT

An item which seems to come 'alive' when it is being folded is the v-belt—particularly one with a long, large section. As usual, there is a right and a wrong way. As the combine is one machine which goes in for belts of this size and temperament, this aid makes a fitting end to storing the combine for the winter.

Fig 1  Hold the belt firmly on the ground and twist inside out.

Fig 2  Keep twisting for one complete turn.

Fig 3  Pull up until the two ends come together.

Fig 4  Fold the ends over each other and the belt will then concertina into a compact coil.

# HEDGE CUTTING IN SAFETY

Regular inspection, knowing what to look for, the day to day sharpening procedure, and deciding when to send a blade to a saw doctor or timber man for attention, are equally important.

A copy of the appendix to the handbook giving the profiles and tooth specification of the blades should go with the blade for repairs. This will tell the saw doctor all he wants to know.

Blades should be inspected twice a day for cracks and tension, and always after hitting stones or metal or overheating. Test by sight and sound. Strike the blade with a piece of wood. Get to know the true 'ring' of your blade. A blade which has lost its tension or temper will ring at a lower note. A cracked blade will sound 'flat' and the ringing tone will not persist. If the note of the blade has changed do not use it until it has been passed as sound by a saw doctor.

Sharpen a little and often or it will become a major operation for an expert.

Do not change the shape of the teeth or make sharp corners at the roots. Use as a guide the profiles in the appendix of the handbook. Note the curved gullets.

Use a round rat-tail file for the gullets. Avoid flat files or a flat disc on a power tool, as these will leave a sharp corner and create a stress point. Heating caused by the power tool will also draw the temper.

The hammering a blunt blade receives from the hedge, and loss of temper due to overheating, increases stress. If this is concentrated at a stress point a hair-line crack may develop.

With slasher blades make sure the tip of the tooth's cutting edge has not been worn away and become rounded. If necessary grind away the circumference of the blade, so as to make sure that the tip of the cutting edge—not the circumference of the blade—makes first contact with the wood. Use a slow-speed grindstone not a power tool—this avoids overheating.

It is important to remember that slasher blades have no 'set' and must never be given one.

With saw blades make sure that all the teeth are the same size and shape and have the same

An example of a badly maintained sawblade—the profile is incorrect, it has a broken tooth, and the square shows 'blueing' caused by overheating.

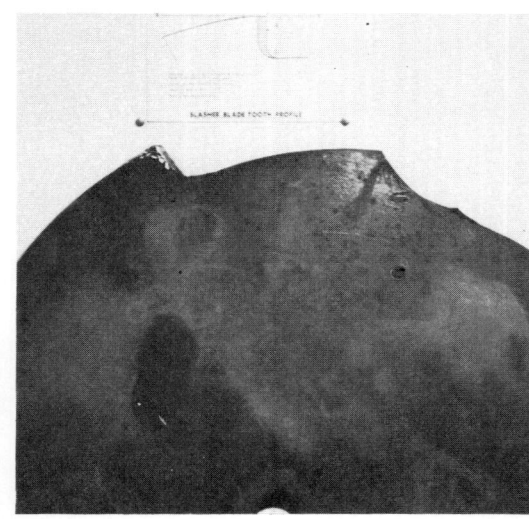

This slasher blade has incorrect profile and worn cutting edges built up by welding. The heat of the welding flame will have caused the blade to lose its temper, the wrong profile has caused shock loading, and several teeth have broken off.

'set' in accordance with the manufacturer's instructions. This is to ensure that no single tooth takes excessive load.

The correct set for the teeth of the McConnel Shapesaw saw blade, for example, is 0.6 to 0.75 mm. Depth of the set should be no more than 12 mm. Never start the set from the root of the tooth.

Lack of set leads to overheating and 'blueing' of the blade, which destroys temper. If this happens the blade must go back to a saw doctor for heat treatment 'hammering.'

The importance of the correct remedial treatment stems from the make-up of the blade. It is forged from a single billet of high alloy steel and not cut out of a sheet, as is popularly believed. This gives a radial flow to the grain in the steel. The blade is then cut out, heated to release stresses, hardened and tempered to the required toughness. After sharpening around the edge, it is 'hammered' by the saw smith to expand the centre but not the outer section, to put into the blade preloaded tension which stops it flapping at high speed. Finally, the surface is ground at low speed without heat to remove marks and enable it to be inspected.

The law allows one broken tooth to be filed down and the saw re-used, but it first needs inspection by a saw doctor to see that other hidden damage has not been caused by the blow which broke the tooth.

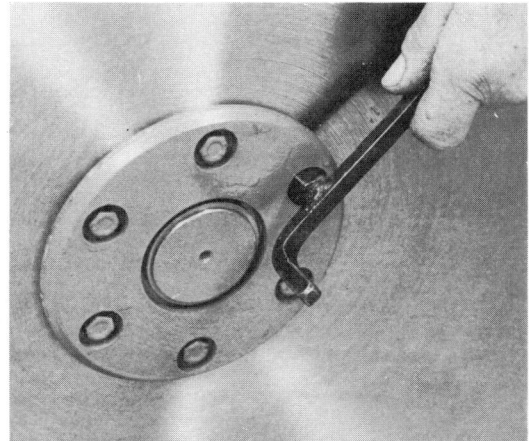

Make sure blades are fitted tightly. Fit the blade, add the retaining plate and locking ring, fit bolts and tighten the nuts hard. Run the blade in a hedge for five minutes, stop and retighten the nuts. In some cases up to $1\frac{1}{2}$ turns can be taken up after 'bedding in.'

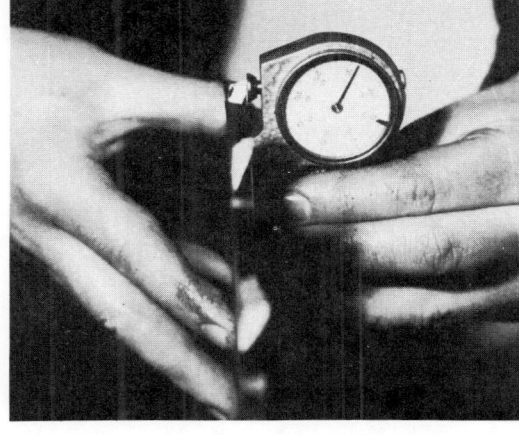

This is the special gauge for checking the 'set' of a McConnel Power Arm Shapesaw blade showing the correct 'set'—0.75 mm. This 'set' must not start at the root of the tooth and should never be more than 18 mm deep. Sharpened blades have no 'set' and should never be given one.

Many firms do not advise working with even one tooth short. Better, they say, to have all teeth removed, a new set recut all round and the blade re-treated. This is usually only half the cost of a new blade.

## BEFORE OPERATING AND BREAK-DOWNS

### THE BALER

If the pick-up baler was not thoroughly checked before haymaking, look it over before harvest.
If it is to stand idle for a time, protect shiny parts and pull out material left in the bale-chamber. Before using the baler trip the knotters and turn the baler over slowly by hand to make sure all moving parts are free. Check that the pto shafts slide easily and the guards are in position. Look at the universal couplings for cracks or missing dust caps.

Make sure the pto clutch plates and wearing surfaces are smooth and rust-free and renew where necessary (1). Check the flywheel clutch torque figure, using a long bar and a spring balance to correct poundage. Ensure the over-run clutch pawls and springs are in good order. Push a shearbolt through the flywheel to check wear between bolt and flywheel; too much wear will allow the bolt to shear before its set torque and give poor density bales, besides being expensive on bolts.

Look for wear on ram bearings and runners and adjust the ram centrally in the balechamber.

This alignment of the ram is one of the most important basic adjustments on the baler. It is also often completely neglected. Correct bearing adjustment is needed to ensure that the ram runs parallel to the bale chamber with the correct clearance or 'play' on the runners at top and bottom over the full length of travel. Excessive or uneven play causes increased power consumption, increased vibration and may upset the smooth running of the rest of the baler. See that the ram-stop enters the balechamber when the needles are in. Adjust the clearance between the ram knife and the stationary knife to the maker's specification, using shims to pack out if necessary (2).

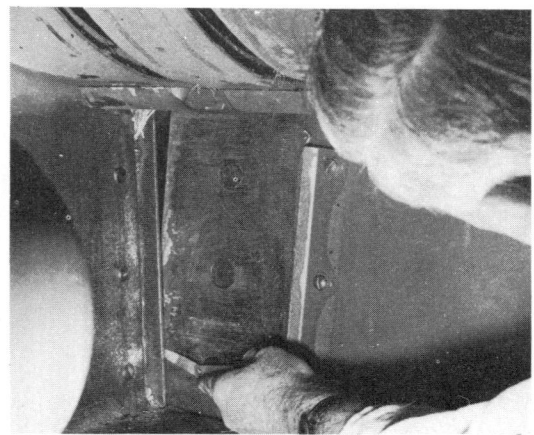

(1)

(2)

(3)

Inspect the knotters for wear on the bill-hooks, retainers, twine-fingers and cam-bearings, and see that the twine knives are sharp (3). The number of stoppages caused by knotter breakdowns is far greater than in any other part of the baler. Look at the needles for a groove where the string is pulled through each time it enters the balechamber. Braze the needles as shown (4) and they will last another season. Use a wire-brush on the knotter brake disc to remove all rust and oil.

Oil the bale tension adjuster threads and check the springs for cracked or broken coils. Have a look at the feeder mechanism for faulty bearings and tines. Turn the pickup and replace any broken or badly bent tines. Keep a few spare tines handy as these often snap during the season.

Check all oil levels and tension chains correctly. Go round the machine with a grease-gun removing any blocked nipples and cleaning or replacing them.

Check tyre pressures and see the bale counter has not seized. Renew oil in the gearboxes, and lay in a stock of correct shear-bolts and string.

Run the baler up to speed and bale some dry straw to remove rust and any stiffness from the ram and balechamber.

### SHEAR BOLT SENSE
By replacing the manufacturer's specified fly-wheel shear bolt with a stronger one you may increase the performance of your baler. But damage to the balechamber, gearbox, needles or ram could occur because of overloading.

Shear bolts are made to fail at a load determined by the designer. They protect the rest of the machine, so always use the manufacturer's shear bolts.

Buy sufficient to last a season and see there are some in the tool-box.

The shear bolt insert in the flywheel is hardened, but will eventually wear and become a loose fit. The bolt may then shear before it should, giving a decreased output from the baler. Before each season check the wear on the insert with a new shear bolt. As a guide, if the bolt hole

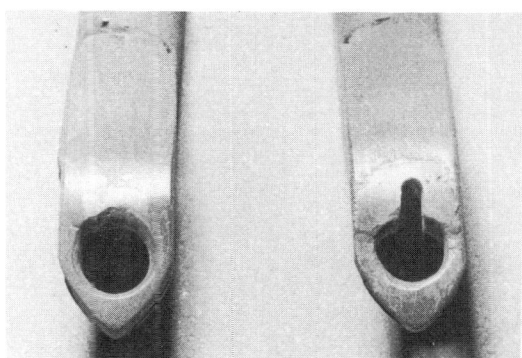

(4)

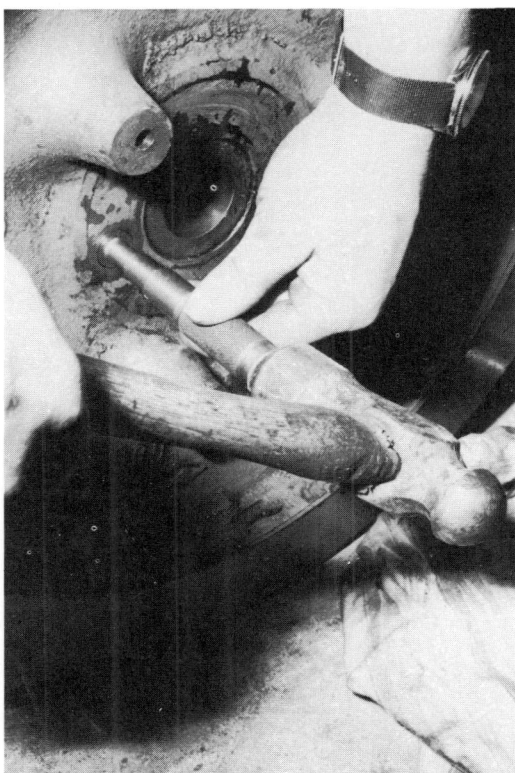

Fitting the new insert.

is noticeably oval the bolt should be replaced.

Before refitting a new one check it and the hole it fits for burrs and remove all dirt from both parts. Use a parallel punch with a large shoulder to fit the new insert. A block of hardwood will suffice if no punches are available. Do not use a taper punch, which may burr the edges and cause the bolt to become jammed.

Tap in the insert until it is flush with the front face of the flywheel. It should not protrude or it will take some of the load instead of the shear bolt. Always use two ring spanners for tightening shear bolts, to avoid injury.

One last time-saving tip: carry a small punch and hammer to knock out broken shear bolts.

Tension all chains correctly, check the pickup reel for broken or missing tines, inspect ram bearings and runners for wear, and grease the machine regularly.

*Photograph copyright by Peter Adams.*

### IN-THE-FIELD CURES FOR BALER BREAKDOWNS

To many of us baler knotters are a mystery and until they go wrong they are best left alone, otherwise they may be incorrectly adjusted and give constant trouble.

NIAE user test reports show that correctly set up knotters will give little trouble. In the chart on the next pages are nine of the most common causes of knotter breakdown and some of their remedies, all of which can be carried out by a skilled tractor driver.

It will pay to have knotters checked over by your dealer just before the baling season begins.

Remember a baler will still function, though inefficiently, with a blunt shearing knife or incorrectly set slip clutches, but if the knotters are wrong it will not begin to bale.

| FAULT | CAUSE | CURE |
|---|---|---|
| 1. Twine cut or broken without a knot being formed | (a) Insufficient twine being drawn through retainer to form knot | (a) Clean retainers of dirt. Adjust tension on retainer spring |
| | (b) Twine cut by sharp edges on retainer | (b) Smooth rough edges on retainer |
| 2. Long end on one side of knot | (a) Blunt twine knife | (a) Sharpen |
| | (b) Knife arm has insufficient lift to cut both twines | (b) Carefully bend knife arm casting to increase lift on knife arm |
| 3. Twine tangles or breaks in spools | Twine tensioner grips twine too tightly | Ease off twine tension out of twine box |
| 4. Twine breaks at knot | Knot breaks on release from bale-chamber | Slacken bale-chamber tension |
| 5. Twine slips off one side of the bale | (a) Packing of bale not even | (a) Adjust packer fingers or wad board to give even density bale |
| | (b) Bale-chamber tensioners unevenly adjusted | (b) Adjust tensioners to give equal tightness on both strings |
| 6. Both ends untied | (a) Twine not held tightly enough by knotter-hook jaw for knot to be formed | (a) Strained hook-jaws. Replace |
| | (b) Knotter-hook tension inadequate | (b) Increase tension |
| 7. Knot stays on knotter hook | (a) Too much tension on knotter-hook | (a) Ease off knotter hook tension |
| | (b) Knife too close to retainer face | (b) Increase distance between knife and retainer face |
| | (c) Stripper arm not lifting knot off hook | (c) Bend stripper to lightly touch knotter-hook |
| 8. Slip knot leaving loop on retainer end of twine | (a) Needle not laying twine over knotter-hook | (a) Increase needle travel |
| | (b) Twine too slack on leaving spools | (b) Increase twine tension out of twine box |
| | (c) Plunger spring broken | (c) Replace |
| | (d) Too much plunger-head clearance between plunger top and bale-chamber | (d) Adjust plunger rollers or guides to correct clearance |

| FAULT | CAUSE | CURE |
|---|---|---|
| 9.  Slip knot leaving loop on needle end only | (a)  Dirty retainer cones<br>(b)  Twine-knife cutting too early<br>(c)  Twine retainer tension too weak<br>(d)  Twine not held in position between | (a)  Clean cones<br>(b)  Locate twine knife correctly<br>(c)  Adjust twine retainer tension<br>(d)  Clean retainer plates |
| 10.  Shear bolts breaking continually | (a)  Fly-wheel clutch incorrectly adjusted<br>(b)  Wrong grade of shear-bolt<br>(c)  Bale-chamber tension excessive<br>(d)  Incorrect pto speed | (a)  Check clutch adjustment<br>(b)  Fit recommended bolts<br>(c)  Ease off bale chamber tension springs<br>(d)  Run tractor at recommended pto speed |
| 11.  Rough edged bales | Knife incorrectly adjusted or blunted | Sharpen knife and adjust clearance |
| 12.  Crop left on ground | (a)  Pick-up height incorrect<br>(b)  Tines missing or broken | (a)  Adjust<br>(b)  Replace |

## DRILL MAINTENANCE

Many drills will be brought out in the middle of March for the first time since last season. A little attention to correct setting up and regular daily maintenance could save money, time and breakdowns.

If the drill was put away properly at the end of last season the hoppers should be clean and free of corrosion. Feed mechanisms, slip clutches and wheel bearings should also have been checked last year—now is not the best time to be chasing spares.

The movable fertiliser feed parts—star wheels and their gear assemblies—should be removed from their winter storage in creosote or diesel

Seed and fertiliser feed spouts, whether metal or plastic, should be checked for damage before use.

oil and refitted to the hopper.

The feed spouts to the coulters should be re-checked—for holes and splits in the case of rubber and plastic and corrosion and distortion on the metal type.

If a large area is to be sown with one particular type, variety or batch of seed, it is worth calibrating the machine to make sure that the correct amount of seed is being drilled.

Many farmers argue that this operation is unnecessary, but a practical example speaks for itself. A Lincolnshire farmer using the manufacturer's recommended setting on a large batch of seed for a 40 hectare piece of land decided to check. His calibration showed that the machine was sowing over 60 kg a hectare too much. Almost 2.5 tonnes of seed were being wasted on the whole operation.

The ideal way to calibrate is with bags attached to the cut-of-work spouts while running in the field to be drilled, but fields vary and a proper stationary test gives a good basic guide. Our picture sequence shows the method. Remember, however, that tests at Edinburgh University show that wheel slip on the drill in the field may be over 20%.

Most drills have a drive cog for high seed rate and low seed rate cog to the feed mechanism and the gear box and finer feed settings step the rate up and down in 7 kg stages.

To avoid wasting seed and land, markers must be set up correctly, Some drivers prefer centre marking, others side marking; our diagrams show the setting method for both.

For trouble-free operation all disc coulter bearings should be greased twice daily and all the other grease points once a day. Aim to force grease into the bearing until the dirt laden grease is forced out.

To keep the fertiliser side free of trouble either fill the hopper at the end of the day's work or empty it and brush it out. The first method is safe if you are confident that the weather will allow you to get back to the job next day but use the second if the weather looks threatening, otherwise you will have a box full of slurry.

The number of wheel turns necessary to travel a tenth of a hectare is calculated using the formula:

$$\frac{10,000}{\text{sowing width (m)} \times \text{diameter of wheel}}$$

Mark a wheel spoke and the drill before turning the required number of turns.

Many modern drills are now equipped with a handle and calibration tray which can be used without having to jack up the drive wheel of the drill.

The seed side of the machine should not give much trouble as long as you keep the seed bag labels and pieces of paper bag out of the hopper. Check daily that both seed and fertiliser are getting into the ground.

The seed collected is then weighed. This weight multiplied by 10, plus an addition of 20% to allow for wheel slip, will give the rate per hectare. As the amount of wheel slip is not known during this static test, the only way to really calibrate accurately is to tie a plastic bag over several seed spouts and drive up and down the field where drilling is to actually work. The weight of seed gained, multiplied up, will give the actual rate per hectare.

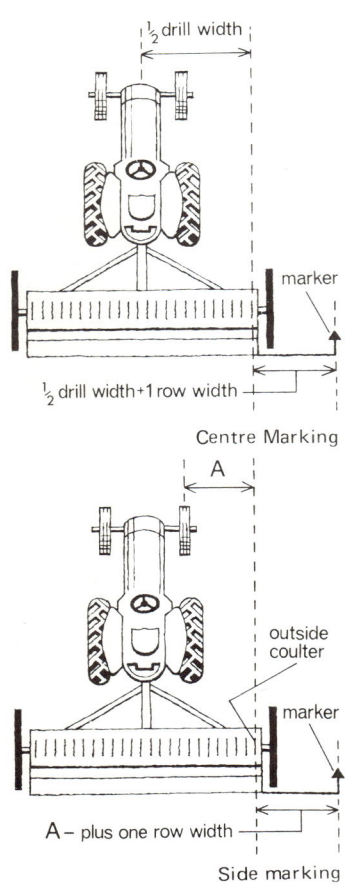

½ drill width

marker

½ drill width +1 row width

Centre Marking

A

outside coulter

marker

A – plus one row width

Side marking

## DYE MARKER FOR SPREADING ACCURACY

Mr. Alan Kyle, Lisahoppin House, Omagh, County Tyrone, Northern Ireland, has come up with a simple inexpensive, home-made device that marks the ground with dye as the tractor drives across a field spreading fertiliser.

This has solved a problem for Mr. Kyle who has been taking three silage cuts for several years, and for any farmer spreading fertiliser immediately after cutting silage. The white stubble makes it difficult for the tractor driver to see the tracks on the previous run.

Dye dripping on to one wheel of the tractor marks the stubble and enables the driver to get an even spread of fertiliser on his next run.

Using an 8 m oscillating spout, Mr Kyle finds 90 litres of diluted dye will mark about 3 hectares.

Crystal violet dye can be bought at the local chemist's shop. A heaped teaspoonful in 20 litres of water makes a suitable concentration.

The bottom part of an old can was mounted on the tractor and a 20 litre oil drum fitted with a tap was placed in it. A rubber hose from the tap drips the dye on to the front wheel. An open-shut valve is operated by a wire from the driver's seat.

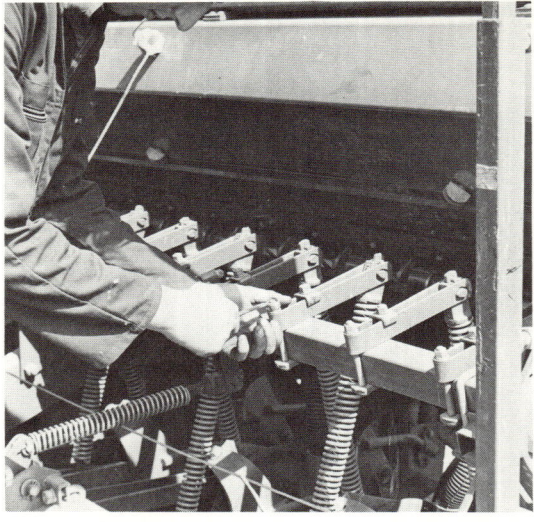

Daily maintenance is obviously important on the drill; of particular importance is the smooth and even functioning of coulters.

## FORAGE HARVESTERS

To prepare the harvester for work go over each grease point making sure that the new grease forces out the old, then wipe the points clean. Check the gear box oil and top up. Remember to look again every 50 hours and drain and refill every 200 hours. Wash chains in paraffin, replace and lubricate with SAE 90 gear oil applied on the top side of the lower chain span. Adjust to allow 10 mm slack for each 300 mm between sprockets. If it is too tight it will overload the bearings; if too slack it may jump off a sprocket or mount a tooth and break. Belts should be well tensioned to transmit the considerable power. Allow no more than 20 to 30 mm up and down movement

Belt tension check. Note 20 to 30 mm play between pulleys but no more.

between pulleys. Slip clutches tend to stick after storage. Free them by slackening the adjustment bolts and turning unit by hand until the clutch slips. Then retighten each bolt the same amount until the clutch does not slip under load. Inflate tyres to recommended pressure.

Broken or damaged flails must be replaced, as should any worn down more than 10 mm or they will not create sufficient wind to blow material up the chute. An equal number must be put on each rod to maintain balance. Flail tips can usually be sharpened by grinding. Hold the flail against the emery wheel so that it is ground back about 8 mm at an angle to give a sharp edge. Take

Close-up of a sharpened flail.

the same amount of each flail to keep the rotor balanced. The shear bar is usually adjustable. Set the clearance between it and the flails according to the degree of laceration and length of cut required—18 mm from the tips of the flails for beet tops and 6 mm for grass. Check this clearance periodically and as the flails wear down, adjust the shear bar accordingly.

For safety do not stand in front of a flail harvester particularly when a low cut is being made where there are a lot of stones about.

On the double-chop type forager with cutting flails and flywheel mounted knife cutters, the same flail procedure should be followed to check condition and sharpness and replace any broken, bent, or badly worn. Check retaining bolts daily and tighten to 240—250 newton metres of torque. The knives and paddles on the cutting head must be equally spaced—two knives with two paddles and so on. Each knife is usually adjustable to the shear plate by loosening and tightening two nuts. Adjust to 1.5 mm from the plate and tap each bolt head with a hammer to ensure it is seating tightly and tighten both nuts securely.

Set paddle clearance between tips and casing 3 to 4.5 mm. If a knife is bent it can be removed and hammered out but do not strike the specially hardened edges. Shear plate must be kept sharp and adjusted as blunt cutting edges and excessive clearance waste power and mangle the crop.

Never inspect or adjust while the machine is in motion. Turn mechanism by hand to see that it is free-moving before running it under power.

The cylinder chopper is similar in action to the knife cutting unit of a lawn mower. The knives must be spaced equally throughout the cylinder otherwise the cutterhead will be out of balance and uniform length of cut will be impossible. The number of knives decides the length of cut and when changing them the knife support as well as the knife must be removed. Knives must be kept sharp and shear bar adjusted to 0.04 mm from them. Failure to maintain these will give poor quality cutting, raise power consumption and increase wear of both knives and shear bar.

When a stone knife sharpener is incorporated it must be held against each blade and moved along its length while the pto drives the cutting cylinder at about $\frac{3}{4}$ speed. Then adjust the shear bar to the sharpened knives after removing it and clearing out material which has collected there. Wear safety goggles during sharpening.

Forage harvesters are power consuming. The faster a flail rotor turns the greater is the demand upon the tractor engine. The two must be matched so that the recommended rotor speed is achieved at the tractor's rated speed. The size of tractor required depends upon the width of cut, forward speed and crop density. Rotor speeds may vary between 1,000 and 1,500 rpm and the tractor and harvester should have some power in hand in order to maintain output under varying operating conditions. The gear which gives the required pto speed without labouring the engine should be chosen and any inequalities in crop density overcome by taking a narrower cut rather than by reducing forward speed. The height of cut of most machines is adjustable from about 25 to 150 mm and the harvester must be set so that it is level in both directions. Skids are there to protect the rotor should the wheels drop into a hollow and these should be set to give a clearance of between 50 to 75 mm between them and the ground.

## A ROUTINE CHECK FOR THE FORAGE HARVESTER

The forage harvester's rotor must be properly balanced, otherwise it will consume extra power and damage the bearings.

On many models the rotor is dynamically balanced before the machine leaves the factory, to give smooth, easy running and prevent excess wear on the rotor bearings.

Broken or missing flails are common causes of poor balancing, so before the season begins check the rotor and flails.

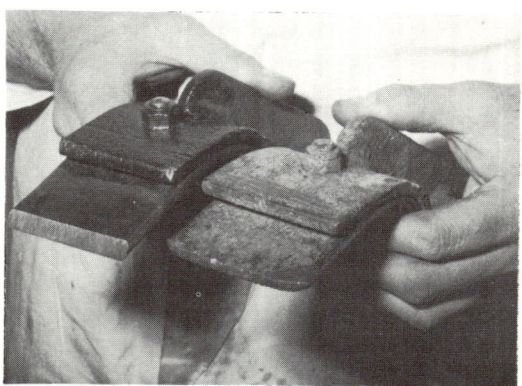

Two flails—one properly reground, the other well worn.

Most rotors have the flails in banks or rows. Remove one row at a time and inspect for loose or missing hardware, bent or broken flails and cracks.

A replacement flail must be hacksawed back to the length of the others or it will cut a different length. Some flails wear more than others and some at a different angle. Grind them all to within about 3 mm of each other. The edge, when sharp, should be parallel to the ground when the flail is hanging vertically from the rotor. Too long an edge will give a weak blade tip that will easily break off.

Before attaching the flails to the rotor, inspect the hardened bushes on which the hammer rotates for splits and wear, and also the bolt

Grinding a flail to the correct cutting angle.

An example of inconsistent grinding (left) and an over-long edge (right) compared with a perfect flail in the centre.

that holds the complete flail to the rotor. The flail should rotate round the bush, but often the bush rotates round the bolt, wearing out the bolt. This is caused by not tightening the bolt sufficiently.

Finally take out the shear plate and sharpen it on the grindstone. Set it in the field, according to length of chop and laceration required. Check belt tension and alignment and gearbox oil levels. And lubricate all grease points.

## COMBINE CARE

Even if your combine is still in the same state as when it finished work last year it is not too late to ensure that when conditions are right it is ready for action.

The operator's manual is the best guide but to supplement this here are a few faults to look out for and remedy.

Look for loose nuts and bolts or damaged threads. Examine split pins for signs of wear. They may look small and unimportant but they do an important job.

Go round the machine with a grease gun making sure all the old grease is pumped out. A leaky nipple can sometimes be cured by putting a rag between the gun and nipple to act as a seal.

If it still leaks, renew it. Make sure sealed bearings have no ruptured seals.

Check sprockets for signs of 'Hooking'—excessive wear on one side of the teeth—which will wear out a chain quickly. When refitting chains replace the spring clips on the connecting links with the open end facing away from the direction of rotation. Do not overtighten but leave enough play to be able to move the link across the sprocket after tightening.

Free the friction clutches and check the linings. It is also worth rotating the 'clapper' clutches to break any rust seal. These are vital safety checks which could save you a lot of money.

Examine the grain and returns elevators for damaged flights. If a link has to be taken out of the chain, fasten the ends with string to prevent it falling down the box.

Get in a stock of spares such as belts, knife sections, reel tines and lifters and a selection of chain links. If your machine is new this year, the dealer may well have a sale-or-return kit of spares which experience has shown to be the most widely used.

If the combine has warning lights or bells which have not flashed or rung yet, check that they are still working. Make sure the relief driver knows his way round the controls and adjustments of a new machine.

This Vee-belt looked all right, but closer inspection revealed that the cords were showing underneath. Renew a belt if it gets into this state, or if oil or sunlight have perished it.

(Centre above)
This is how the drum bars should look. Wire brush them to get all the dirt out and empty the stone trap.

(Centre below)
Check over hydraulic hoses for cracks and leaks at the connections and make sure ram seals are sound. Top up the hydraulic oil reservoir.

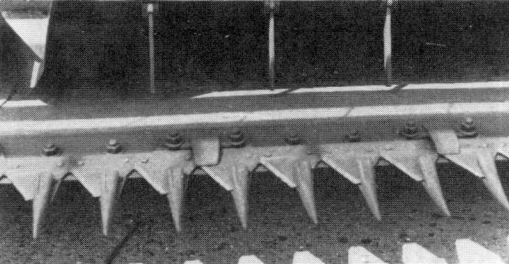

Set up the cutter bar as for a mower, replacing broken or loose sections. If knife register is incorrect, it is usually adjusted by removing or adding shims at the cutter head drive assembly. Check the retractable tines on the auger. If they are loose, or if any bearings are worn, replace them.

Use a wire brush to clean the sieves and oil the linkages that allow the louvre angle to be altered.

## HOW TO SET UP THE COMBINE'S DRUM

The drum is the heart of the combine. Bad setting and maintenance will give a poorly threshed sample with a low selling price. The main things to look for in a preseason check are damaged or badly worn rasp bars, drum balance and speed and concave clearance.

First clean out all the dust and dirt. Wire brush the rasp bars to remove caked dirt between the serrations.

Next remove all the drives to the drum and spin it slowly, listening for squeaks or grating sounds that will indicate a damaged bearing. Check that there are no tight spots in the bearings and no sideways and up and down movement.

To check wear on the rasp bars fit a new attachment bolt in an old bar. This will stand proud of the bar and if the bolt protrudes more than **6 mm replace the whole set of bars, because** wear will have occurred on all of them. When fitting new bars make sure the serrations face alternate ways.

Checking drum balance is important, because the drum revolves at 1,000—1,400 rpm and if it is unbalanced the bearings will be ruined and other expensive damage to the drum and concave may occur.

Chalk numbers on the bars of the drum and spin it lightly, noting which bar stops at the top. Repeat three times. If any one bar stops at the top all three times, weight needs adding to that

Before balancing, identify each blade with a chalked number.

Trial balancing is effected by sticking washers to the lightest bar with grease.

bar to keep it equal in weight to the others. Add weight by sticking flat washers to the bar with grease.

Spin the drum again to check, moving the washers about until the drum is properly

Spin drum to test balance. If one bar stops at the top repeatedly, it should be weighted.

balanced. Bolt the washers to the back of the bar and recheck.

If only one bar is badly damaged, through stones or metal getting into the drum, also replace the opposite bar to maintain drum balance. Replacing one bar on an old combine will lead to bad threshing because the concaves will have to be set to the new bar and this will give under-threshing of the corn. Narrowing the concave gap will cause the new bar to hit the concave bar and cause more damage.

## HARROW CARE

Harrows must rate among the toughest and often the most ill-used pieces of equipment on the farm. Fortunately they are usually built to take it, but care in use and treatment can mean better work and a longer life.

There are scores of types but, generally, those with shorter **60 mm tines should be used on grass and the 110 mm tined units kept for arable. Un-less there is a very thick matt of grass the longer** tines will tend to jump about and do little good. Best speed is **6 to 7 kmph to let the harrow do its** work rather than the highest possible gear at full throttle.

Take greater care using a new harrow. The sharper tines will bite more than a worn set. Pull away gently—jerky starts soon result in some-thing breaking.

Harrows should not be loaded with sleepers or other weights to make the harrowing effect more severe, nor should they be pulled sideways through a gateway. Both actions cause excessive loads on the links.

If a link breaks, repair it at once with links of the correct size—otherwise more strain will be put on the surrounding links, setting up a chain reaction of breakages. If the job needs two harrows in tandem take the towing chain of the rear harrow over the front one and attach it direct to the tractor—don't just hitch it to the harrow in front.

Check harrow drawbars or whippletrees for alignment. If they are bent, more strain is placed on a few pulling points. Careless driving through gateways or near banks, posts, trees and other solid objects is the main cause of bent drawbars.

Hydraulic lift mounted harrows can serve two purposes. A heavy harrow can be made lighter by slightly raising the linkage and, on dirty ground, flexible harrows are much easier to clean.

If repairs become necessary remember that flexible harrows are usually made of high carbon steel and cannot be welded. To fit new links, heat the link where required and fit it to the harrow. Do not cool it using water or it will become brittle and fracture. Let it cool naturally.

## REPAIR OF TRAILER HOSES

Trailer hydraulic hoses are often snapped through drivers forgetting to disconnect them from the tractor or the pipe fouling the tractor linkage. If the break is near the end of the pipe the coupling can be taken off and refitted to the pipe. This is a simple workshop job, but cleanness is essential as dirt entering the joint could cause leaks in the connections or damage the seals.

Hold the hose in the vice and square up the broken end of the pipe. Use a fine-toothed hacksaw for this job and also to cut the outside rubber coating to the wire braiding, taking care not to damage the wire and weaken the pipe (1).

Slit the rubber cover with a sharp knife and peel it off. Next, screw the female end of the coupling on to the pipe (2) until the hose just bottoms in the fitting. The female half of the coupling has a left-hand thread. Before fitting the insert lightly lubricate the threads and the inside of the hose, to avoid twisting or tearing the hose and to assist assembly. Still holding the pipe in the vice, screw the insert into the female half until the nut on the insert bottoms on the coupling (3). The insert is tapered and will tighten the hose against the female half as it is screwed on, making an oil-tight seal.

Screw the tractor coupling on to the insert and tighten up (4). When refitted to the trailer and operational, inspect for leaks.

(1)

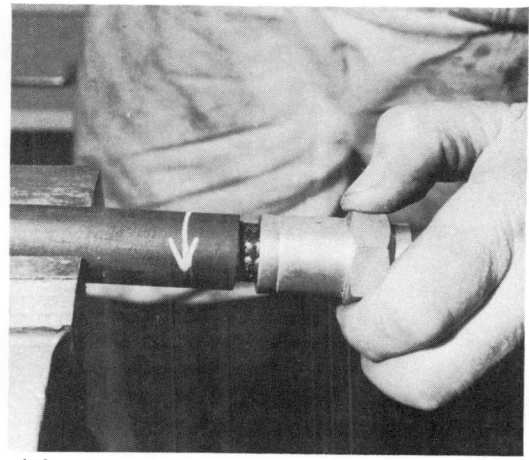

(2)

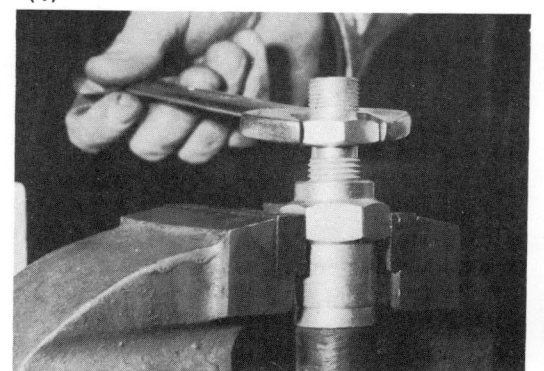

(3)

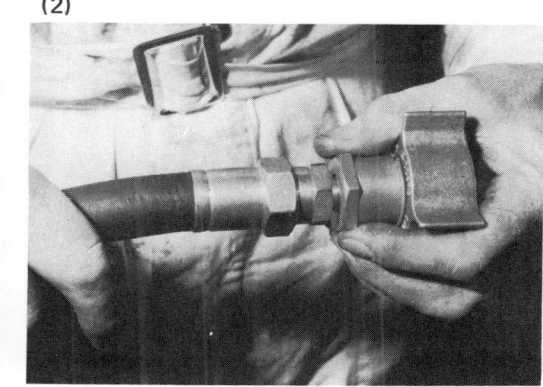

(4)

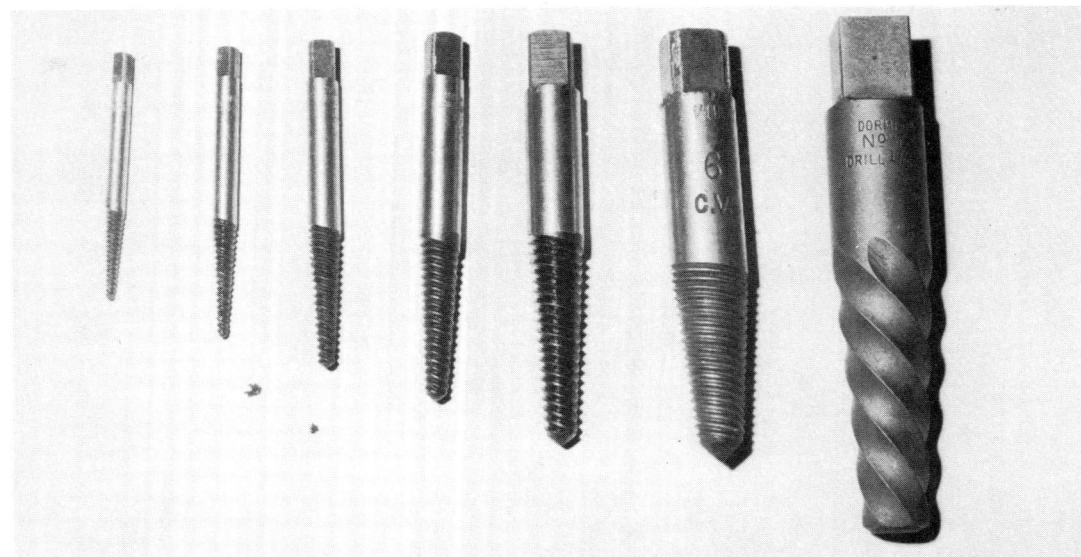

Choose a stud extractor to match the size of stud and the hole drilled in it.

## EXTRACTING STUBBORN BROKEN STUDS

Studs and bolts are often broken off in their threaded holes by using too much force on the spanner when tightening up. Removing the broken portion from the hole can present problems.

Stud extractors will remove studs protruding above the surface, such as cylinder head studs, but they are expensive and some damage the threads. A slower but cheaper method is to use two nuts locked on the thread one against the other. Use a spanner on the bottom nut and turn the stud out.

Several other ways of removal can be tried. Use a pair of grips and try to twist out the stud. Failing that, weld a nut to the top of the broken portion.

If you have no nuts handy, weld a piece of bar across the stud and use it as a handle to turn the stud and remove it from the hole.

When the stud breaks below the surface try to undo it by turning it with a punch until it is above the surface.

If it is too far below the surface for this method drill a hole through the centre of the stud and use a sunken stud extractor, which is a steel tapered bolt with a coarse left-hand thread. It is held in a tap wrench and threaded into the hole through the stud. Because of the taper the

Insert the appropriate extractor and twist anti-clockwise.

Drill right through the stud, preferably using a vertical drilling machine.

extractor tightens up in the hole and the left-hand thread will undo a right-hand thread stud or bolt.

It these methods fail, drill the stud right out and rethread the hole. If the casting is a cheap one gas-cut the stud out, but you must be right first time or the casting will be ruined.

# MAINTENANCE

## BRAKE ADJUSTMENT

First step is to jack up the tractor wheel. Tighten the brakes, using a screwdriver through the adjustment slot. This will centralise the shoes and ensure the whole area is in contact with the brake drum, so that it will come away from the drum evenly when it is slackened off.

Slacken the adjuster until the wheel will revolve freely without the shoe rubbing on the drum. Carry out the same procedure on the other wheel.

Road-test on a hard, level stretch of road. Lock both independent brake pedals together and drive at about 8 kmph. Brake hard and the tractor should come to a stop in a straight line. If one wheel locks before the other, or the tractor veers to one side, slacken the brake one notch on the offending wheel and re-test. Continue until the brakes are equalised. This can be done with a screwdriver without jacking up the tractor. When the job is complete, make sure the rubber bung or metal plate is replaced in the adjusting slot to prevent water or dirt entering the brake.

Adjust your brakes often if one independent brake is being used regularly, such as muck-loading or turning on the headlands when cultivating. If this is not done regularly, one brake will wear more than the other and when both are used together the unused brake will lock before the other.

Jack up the tractor wheel at a convenient point on the axle.

Locate the brake adjuster, tighten fully with a screwdriver, and slacken until the wheel revolves freely.

## BRAKE SHOE RENEWAL

New brake shoes are usually necessary when either all the adjustment has been taken up, or the shoes are worn to the rivets. In the second case the rivets will score the brake drums if the shoes are not renewed and will impair brake efficiency. It pays to remove the drums occasionally to check wear and blow lining dust out.

To renew the shoes stand the tractor on a hard, level base, block both front wheels and one rear wheel to prevent the tractor rolling off the jack. Release brakes and loosen the adjusters.

Jack up the tractor, remove wheel and place axle stand under the axle as an additional safeguard. Clean dirt off the drum and slacken the screws holding the drum. If these are tight use a small chisel to release them (1). Remove drum. If it is tight tap it gently round the edge with a copper or hide hammer to ease it off (2). Most drums are cast steel or iron and may break if hit with a steel hammer.

Use an air line to blow lining dust from the shoes. Make a drawing of the position of the brake shoes holes in which the springs fit on the shoes, and what colour the springs are. Springs are colour coded according to strength and must be returned to their original position or if exchanged, replaced by one of similar colour.

Springs can be removed by lifting them from the brake shoe with the tip of a screwdriver (3).

1 One way of releasing a tight drum retaining screw is to tap it round with a small chisel.

2 Gently tap the drum with a soft-faced hammer to remove it. Do not hit the backplate.

3 Lever the springs away with a screwdriver, noting which holes they are in.

Remove shoes and adjuster. Clean off dirt from backing plate with paraffin and dry off. Apply a zinc-based grease to all bearing surfaces, shoe pivots and adjuster threads. Do not use ordinary grease as it may run on to the linings.

Replace new shoes and springs according to your diagram. If a strong spring is difficult to re-position, double a piece of baler twine round the spring's hook and wrap the string round your hand. You can then get extra leverage to extend the spring. Remove the string (4) once the spring

4 Strong springs can be pulled into position with the aid of a length of baler twine.

is in position.

Ensure the adjuster turns freely if it is the threaded type and lubricate with a smear of the zinc-based grease. Make sure shoes are correctly fitted, so that when the adjuster expands the shoes expand. Clean dust and grease from the brake drum.

If the drum is badly scored by worn rivets replace it. If the scores are not too deep take it to a dealer who has a lathe and he will skim it and remove the scores. Fit the screws into the drum and tighten them up.

Replace the wheel on the axle and the brakes are ready for adjusting.

## DISC BRAKES

Many tractors are now equipped with wet (oil immersed), inboard-mounted disc brakes. These cannot be inspected or changed from the outside; the axle has to be split. Nevertheless, adjustment to take up wear and keep them 'balanced' is necessary. The free travel on the foot pedal should be adjusted to manufacturer's recommendation and each disc linkage should be adjusted so that the tractor 'pulls straight' when test braked.

## CHAIN REPAIR

Repairing a hook type chain is easy—simply re-move the damaged link by bending the chain and sliding one link from the other. A new link can then be fitted.

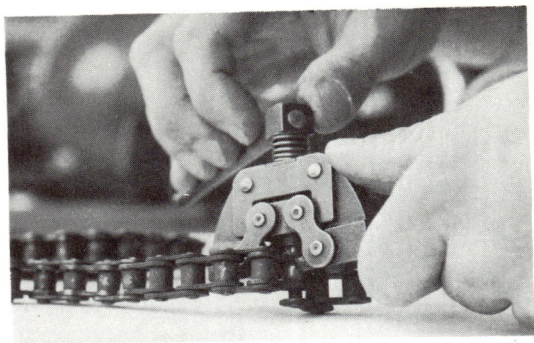

*Pictures by courtesy of Aylesbury College of Further Education.*

Repairing a roller chain is more difficult be-cause of the rivets that join one link to another. It is possible to use a chisel and punch to re-move the pin, but this often results in damage to the other links which causes more trouble.

A quicker and easier way is to use a bearing pin extractor.

After clamping it on to the roller of the pin to be removed, screw the tommy-bar down and push out the pin with the centre punch. A new link can then be fitted.

The same procedure can be used to lengthen or shorten a chain, but, instead of fitting only a connecting link, a cranked link is fitted as well to give the correct length.

The principal chain types; hook-link (top), roller chain (centre) and precision roller chain.

A heavy hook-link chain showing the proper direction of travel.

## CHAIN CARE

Chain drive, common in agriculture, is used mainly where a positive drive is needed.

Three main types of chain are in common use. The hook-link type, made of malleable cast iron or pressed steel, is generally used on low-speedwork with rough cast sprockets.

The roller chain, for higher speed drives, is made of steel treated to resist corrosion and can replace malleable and pressed steel chains. It will run on the same sprockets as malleable chains and in some cases steel chains but a trial fit on the sprocket must be made first.

Lastly there is the precision roller chain, used in high speed applications. It will take higher loads than the other types. An accurately machined sprocket is essential with this chain.

Because of their reliability and simplicity chains are often neglected and cause inconvenient breakdowns. Maintenance is easy with regular inspections to check links and rollers. Lubrication requirements depend on the operating condition. If the chain runs in an oil bath, topping up is all that is required apart from recommended oil-changes.

If a roller chain is operating in dusty conditions, as on a combine, then a graphite grease bath is needed.

First clean off all dirt with paraffin and a stiff brush, moving the joints to ensure that caked dirt inside is shifted.

Heat up some graphite grease in a shallow tray until the grease melts. Immerse the chains in the liquid grease for 10 minutes moving the chains regularly to allow the grease to penetrate all the rollers and links. Then hang up the chain and let it dry off. This will be sufficient lubrication. Never spread oil over a roller chain in

On a roller chain, align the split pins to point forward.

dusty operating conditions; the dust and the oil will form a grinding paste that will rapidly wear the chain out.

For malleable and pressed chains and those in non-dusty conditions simply soak the chain in oil after cleaning and let it drain before refitting.

Wear in malleable or pressed steel chains is easily shown by broken or cracked links and sprockets which must be replaced.

Check roller chain wear by measurement. If over 25 links the chain has worn more than half

The corresponding alignment for links on a precision roller chain.

a link's length, fit a new chain. Check the sprocket for wear— fitting a new roller chain to a worn sprocket is a waste of money. The misshapen teeth will quickly wear the new chain. If the teeth show signs of hooking then renew the sprocket as well.

Tension all types of chain so that there is about half an inch of movement on the slack side with shaft centres about 300 mm apart. Avoid over-tightening chains, or bearings, chain and sprockets will wear excessively.

When fitting chains to the sprockets make sure the connecting link or split pin is fitted the right way as shown in the picture, otherwise the chain may split and fall off. Also make sure that safety guards are replaced after chain adjustments.

*Pictures by courtesy of Aylesbury College of Further Education.*

## COOLING SYSTEM CARE

An hour spent checking the tractor cooling system will help to ensure a troublefree winter. Examining the thermostat, the radiator and the antifreeze are the three main jobs.

The thermostat is a temperature-sensitive valve in the cooling system to allow rapid warm up of the engine and keep it at the correct temperature.

Two main types are in common use, the bellows type filled with a volatile liquid, and the wax-filled thermostat. As the temperature rises the volatile liquid or wax will expand so opening the valve and allowing water to pass from the engine water jacket to the radiator to be cooled for further use.

If a temperature gauge is fitted to your tractor, use it to check the thermostat. Starting from cold, the temperature should build up rapidly and remain constant.

Remove the radiator filler cap after starting the engine from cold and allow it to run at a fast idle. There should be little or no flow of water through the radiator. If there is a flow remove the thermostat to check if it is stuck in the open position.

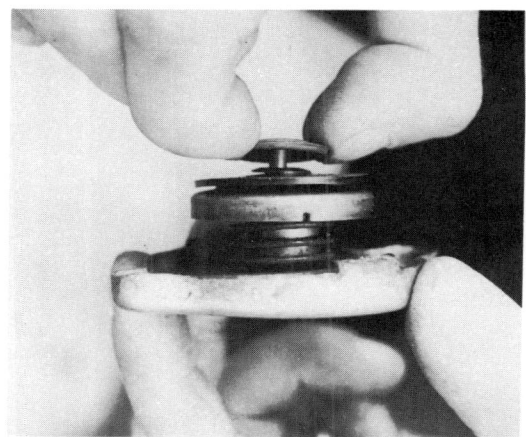

Check that the pressure valve in the filler cap is not jammed by dirt and that the rubber gasket on the cap is in good condition.

If you have no temperature gauge, check the thermostat by removing it from the engine and placing it in a beaker of cold water. Heat it on a cooker and use a thermometer to check at what temperature it begins to open. The correct temperature at which it should open will be stamped on the top. It should start to open within 2 or 3°C of the marked temperature and go on to the fully open position within a further 11 to 14°C.

The two types of thermostat—bellows type on the left and the wax-filled on the right.

The valve on the thermostat on the left is stuck open and will not allow the engine to reach its proper working temperature.

Check that thermostat opens at the right temperature by testing with a thermometer in hot water.

Use an air line to blow out the dirt from the fan side of the radiator—not from the front.

Carefully measure antifreeze in clean containers and mix it with clean water.

After working in harvest fields with plenty of dust and chaff about, the radiator core will soon become blocked with debris as the fan draws air in. Use an airline to blow dirt out from the fan side. Stubborn pieces can be picked out with a length of stiff welding rod.

Open the tap, drain the radiator and back flush it. Do this by removing the radiator cap and bottom hose. Place one end of a hose pipe into the bottom outlet of the radiator, seal the join with some rag. Connect the other end of the hose to the mains water supply. The pressure of the water will move all the bits of rust and dirt and clean out the down tubes. Continue until clean water comes out of the filler cap.

Lastly make sure that the overflow pipe is not blocked and that the filler cap seal is in good condition.

When mixed with water antifreeze lowers the freezing point. A 25 per cent solution—one litre of anti-freeze to three litres of water—is enough to prevent freezing in most UK winter conditions. If in doubt consult your dealer on the correct amount to mix with the water.

Without antifreeze, when water reaches freezing point the ice will expand. Since the cooling system is sealed it will push against the metal of the cylinder block, head and radiator until it finds a weak point, and splits the metal. Frost cracks on an engine are expensive to repair and in most cases the damaged parts need renewing.

It is possible to drain the tractor of water each night but it is a tiresome chore that can easily be forgotten. Put antifreeze in at the beginning of the winter and top up as necessary. Always use the same type and strength of antifreeze as was originally used. Mixing two types may result in a chemical which damages the metal.

Use clean containers to mix antifreeze and water. Refill with the correct mixture until it is an inch from the top. Run tractor for 10 mins and then check level.

Check hosepipes for cracks or splits, renew if necessary and make sure all hose clips are tight. Correctly tension the fanbelt and inspect the fan for missing or bent blades. A fan with a blade missing can damage water pump bearings.

## FIELD MAINTENANCE FOR DISC HARROWS

Disc harrows are among the hardest-working implements on the farm, but properly maintained they will last for years. Routine maintenance in the field should include daily greasing of all the bearings and the pivot points that angle the discs. Try to make sure no dirt stops in bearings by pumping grease in until you see clean grease

Set the scrapers close to the discs.

Tighten discs with stillsons and a spanner.

coming out. Dirt and grease form an abrasive grinding paste that quickly wears out bearings.

Main field adjustments are the top link and tractor lift rod setting for levelling the equipment, and scraper settings. Set scrapers as close to the discs as possible to avoid soil build-up in sticky conditions. Knock bent scrapers back into position with a hammer. If they are badly bent and cannot be straightened with a hammer, take them off the machine, heat the bent portion with a cutting torch and straighten them on the anvil.

Each gang of discs consists of a square centre shaft with each disc separated from its neighbour by a metal spool. Spools and discs are kept tight against one another by a thread and nut on one end of the centre shaft. During work, wear on spool faces and disc centres will cause the discs to become a sloppy fit on the shaft and to wobble. Tighten the nut on the end of the shaft of each gang before this becomes too serious. Use thick flat washers or spacers to take up excess wear at the end of the shaft, otherwise the discs will eventually revolve independently of the shaft instead of with it. The net result will be expensive and unnecessary replacement of discs and shaft. Tightening the discs is a simple job. Hold the end spool nearest the adjusting nut with a pair of stillsons to prevent the shaft revolving and use a ring spanner on the nut.

Replace cast iron bearing centres and caps.

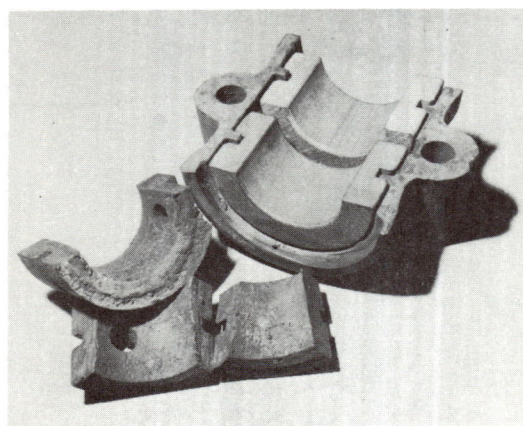

Wooden bearing shells.

Partly-worn disc centre holes may be reduced to their original size and shape by laying them on an anvil, concave side up, and peining with a hammer round the edge of the hole. Clean up the rough edges.

Discs bearings take downward loads from the discs and frame and side or radial loads from the curved discs. Most common types of bearings are chilled cast-iron centres and caps, with flanges on the centres to counteract side loads. Two bolts hold the bearing **together. Another type is a cast-iron centre with replaceable, oil impregnated hardwood shells in the caps.**

With all-cast-iron bearings renew both the centre and the caps. Renewing just the centre is false economy, as wear also occurs on the caps. Putting a new centre in old caps will allow the centre to flop about and wear out rapidly. Wooden shells are cheaper, but will need replacing more often. Make sure all dirt is removed from the caps, otherwise new shells will not seat properly and protrude above the edges of the caps. When you tighten the holding bolts the shells will split.

Other points to check include all hardware on the implement, cracked or chipped discs and wear on the bumper or end plates on each gang, particularly where the ends of the front gangs rub together.

## CHECKING OVER THE BATTERY

The two connections on a battery whether for a tractor, combine harvester or any engine driven machine must be kept clean and tight. Remove each and thoroughly scrape the lead connection and battery terminal until a close metal to metal contact can be made. Before replacing smear the terminals with petroleum jelly or 'Vaseline'; this will help to counteract corrosion. Tighten holding screw or nut and bolt. It is particularly important to obtain a tight fit with the earth lead otherwise the battery will fail to run the starter motor.

Corrosion at the terminals builds up very quickly and if left untouched will eat into them and resist the flow of current, causing loss of power and eventually failure. A corroded connection is extremely hard to remove.

The battery casing. The top of the battery must be kept clean and dry as damp dust causes leakage and battery acid tends to 'creep' and cause the battery to run down. Wipe with a clean rag regularly and if it is in a particularly bad state wash it down with caustic soda and water.

Topping up the cells. Distilled water which is free from impurities should be used so as not to ruin the plates. This water should be kept in a clean bottle or covered container which is insoluble to water, i.e. glass, china, rubber or lead. In order to pour in the water without splashing use a narrow neck filter or one with a rubber tube. Fill each cell to the top of the plates and no farther. The vapour given off in use is water so the addition of this only is needed. When checking water level never use a naked light as the mixture of oxygen and nitrogen given off can be highly explosive. If a battery is over-turned or the contents spilled out then acid will have to be added; and this is normally a job for a garage, where acid of the correct specific gravity can be put in. A 'flat' battery can freeze solid at $-10°$ C but a fully charged one not until the temperature has fallen to $-30°$ C.

Keep the battery well 'up' in cold weather and add the water only when the engine is soon going to be run. The charging will mix the water and acid together before the water lying in a layer on the top freezes.

Measuring instruments. You need an hydrometer for reading the specific gravity of the sulphuric acid solution and a voltmeter. The former should show a reading for each cell of between 1.25 and 1.3 when fully charged. If the reading is below 1.2 the cell is 'flat' and probably useless. This cell then has to be 'fed' by the others and the battery will fail to hold its charge and need

replacing. The voltmeter is for recording voltages but it gives a really accurate reading only when the battery is charging under load. The battery has to do a lot of work on modern tractors and machines and thoroughly deserves the small amount of attention needed to keep it efficient. It thrives on work so never leave a battery idle. Find a use for it or leave it on periodic charge.

## BATTERY CARRIER
This simple battery carrier is made from 'meccano' type angle iron, with a plywood floor and a small pair of wheels bolted to the frame. A length of 25 mm diameter pipe makes a good handle with which to push it around. Use it when you have to move batteries around the workshop, or for taking batteries out to tractors on the farm.

## HOW TO LOOK AFTER VEE-BELTS
Vee-belts consist of woven nylon cords encased in a synthetic rubber compound. Their shape is a truncated vee with an included angle of about 40 degrees between the sides.

The pulleys they drive have a groove of the same shape as the belt. As the belt wears it slips deeper into the pulley to continue driving. The belt should be replaced long before it can touch the bottom.

Correct tension is the vital factor with any type of belt. Too much slack will not allow full power to be transmitted and slip will occur. If the pulley is made of alloy, excess slip will cause heating and grooves will form in the pulley sides. These will soon ruin a new belt. Too tight a belt will cause wear on pulley and motor bearings and fractures in the belt casing and cords.

Movement per 30 cm of distance between the pulleys should be about 12 mm. A properly tensioned belt will have a springy feeling. After initial stretching a belt will not need retensioning for a long time. Do not attempt to overtension a belt in advance to overcome this initial stretching.

Machines such as forage harvesters and mills-and-mixers often have banks of 2, 3 or 4 vee-belts. These consist of matched belts of the same length and if one of them fails the set must be replaced with another matched set. As the belts wear they stretch slightly and replacing one will mean that the new belt will do most of the driving.

When replacing a belt undo the tension adjusters fully to allow the belt to fit over the pulleys. Do not use a screwdriver or tyre lever to get the belt in position, this will weaken the cords and cause fractures in the casing.

If there is no way of telling what length a broken belt was, choose a piece of rope that will sit neatly in the pulley vee, and wrap it round all the pulleys to measure the length. It will give some indication of the length for your dealer. When a new machine is delivered to the farm make a note of numbers printed on the belt. A useful tip is to paint the number on the inside of the guard. When you put a machine away at the end of the season, release the tension on all the belts. This will reduce the amount of 'set' and rough running when you start the machine next time.

A few degrees of misalignment in a belt pulley will shorten belt life. It will cause uneven wear, the belt may roll over in the pulley groove and power transmission will be reduced. Or it may throw all the load on to one side of the belt, causing the cords to stretch on that side.

Use a straight edge to check alignment. Spin the pulleys by hand to see that they are not bent and check for chipped edges.

When the straight edge is laid across both pulleys it should touch all four edges. Adjust the alignment until it does.

With many machines altering the tension also alters alignment, with holes slotted one way to take up fore and aft movement for tension, and the other way for sideways movement for alignment.

Maintenance of belts consists of keeping them free from oil and grease, otherwise they perish, swell and rot. Ensure that the pulleys are in good order. Store belts by hanging from a nail in a dry corner of the workshop out of sunlight. Long belts can be folded and stored flat on a shelf.

## GREASE NIPPLE CLEANER
Grease nipples, and the area around them, have almost a magnetic attraction for dust and dirt and this makes it essential that they are cleaned before the grease gun is applied. If they are not, the dirt on the top of the nipple will be forced into the bearing along with the grease with obvious results. An old tooth brush with its handle removed forms a useful gadget which speeds up the job of cleaning. It is secured to the end of the grease gun (see diagram) by means of two screws (A) screwed into holes drilled through the back of the brush and soldered to the gun. An easier method of fixing the brush, but not as strong as screws, would be to use a synthetic metal adhesive.

This gadget is especially handy for cleaning awkward nipples lurking in corners behind guards.

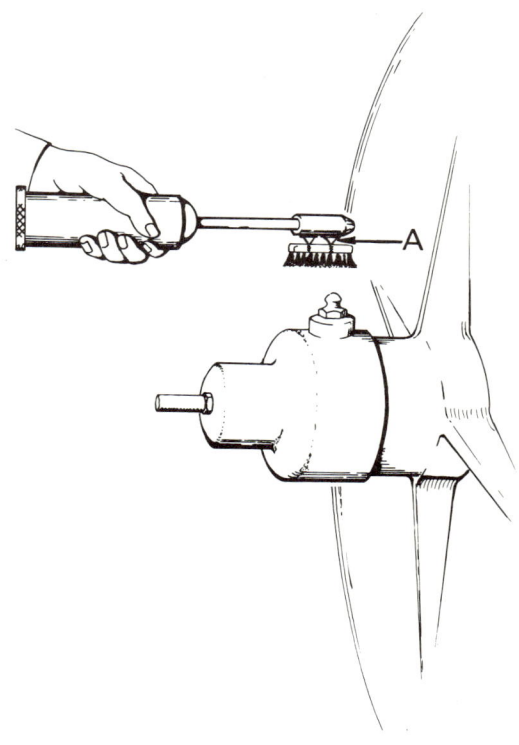

# KEYS AND KEYWAYS

One of the most common ways of joining a gear or sprocket to a shaft so that they revolve together is by means of a key. Temporary fastenings, the keys are always made of steel, as they are subjected to considerable crushing and shearing stress as the shaft turns.

The key is always made of softer steel than the shaft, being cheaper to replace.

A keyway consists of a recess in a shaft or hub to accommodate the key. There are five main kinds of sunken key—square and rectangular taper, square and rectangular parallel, and woodruff.

Taper keys have a standard taper of 1:100. They are measured at the larger end for thickness, are uniform in width and have either square or rounded ends. They are fitted by driving the key into the keyway until the taper tightens against the component and prevents the part from moving.

Taper keys can be difficult to remove. The best method is to knock the sprocket down the shaft, take out the key and pull the sprocket off. This can be difficult if a rust seal has formed between the key and component, or if there is insufficient room to allow the sprocket to be knocked down the shaft. If this happens try **heating the sprocket boss with an oxy-acetylene**

Gib-head keys should be extracted with this home-made tapered drift.

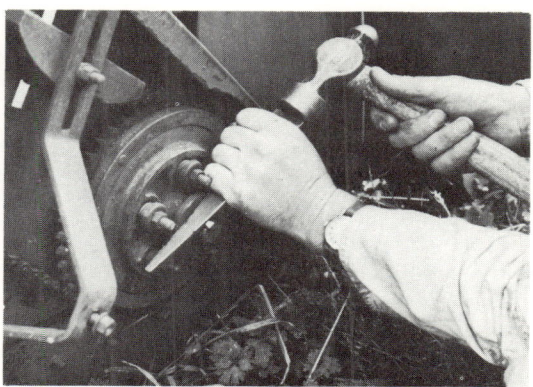

Sharp taps with a hammer soon remove stubborn keys.

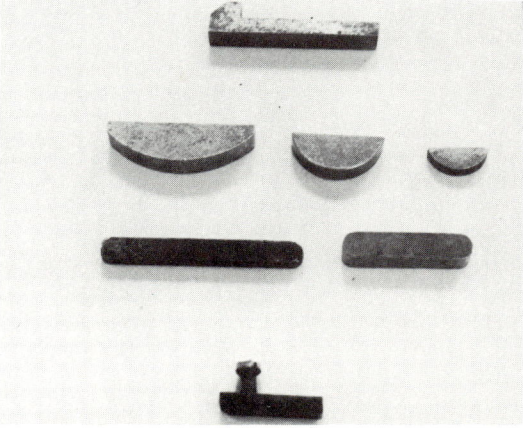

Several types of key—the gib-head, woodruff, parallel and feather, looking from the top.

On the right is a loosely fitted key which began to move in the keyway and became worn.

torch to expand it and pull out the key with pliers or grips.

To prevent these problems arising use a gib-head taper key. This type has a raised head to allow it to be knocked in and prised out without damaging the taper. To extract the gib-head key, make a taper drift out of 6 mm thick steel plate about 150 mm long, 50 mm wide at one end and tapering to 6 mm at the other. Place the narrow end between the key head and component and hit the wider end. The taper on the drift will force out the key without damaging the key or component.

Parallel keys are virtually the same as taper keys except that, as their name implies, they are parallel throughout their length. They are used mainly where a pulley or gear has to slide sideways on a shaft until the belt or chain that fits on it is in line. Then the component can be washered up and held in position by a split-pin.

Main snag with these keys is that they tend to 'fret' or move in the keyway and try to turn over, particularly if the drive is often reversed. This results in wear on both the key and keyway edges, and the key becomes a loose fit in its groove and eventually shears.

Woodruff keys are deeply sunk and are easily adjustable to take up any taper in the hub of the component. They are shaped as part of a circle and the keyway in the shaft is cut on a milling machine to give a recess of the same diameter as the key.

Advantages are that the deep fitting prevents the key turning over, and it will tilt slightly to accommodate any small taper in the boss to which it is fitted. But because of the much deeper keyway the shaft can be weakened at that point.

Other types of key are the feather, which can lock a unit anywhere on a splined shaft, and flat, hollow and round keys, used for light work.

## FITTING A KEY

The secret of fitting a key properly is to ensure that the correct sized key is used for the job and that it fits well in its keyway. A sloppy fit will wear the shoulders on the recess in the shaft or gear hub, and the key will try to run over.

First make sure that the hub fits the shaft. Remove high spots and rust on the shaft with emery cloth and try the hub on the shaft. Next clean up rough edges on the key and shoulders of the keyways with small, fine file and try the key for size.

If the key moves sideways more than a few thous, a larger key is needed. If the shoulders of the recess are badly worn, a new shaft is necessary or the keyway can be recut on another part of the shaft.

Use a flat-ended punch to tap the key into its recess.

Tap the key squarely into its recess. The same amount of the key should be showing above the shaft for the whole of its length. Finally slide the sprocket on the shaft, line the keyway up with the shaft, and tap it over the key until it is in its correct position (see picture next page).

Mr. Brian Parker, welding contractor, 2 Wickstead Close, Kettering, Northants, has evolved a simple method of renovating worn keyways in shafts.

Knock the sprocket on to the shaft and over the key with a soft-faced hammer.

All that is required, he says, is a dummy key made of copper and an electric welder. The copper key needs to be the shape and thickness of a new key.

Place the dummy key tightly in the keyway and build up the shaft on either side of the key with weld. The copper will not fuse with the weld metal and will prevent the keyway being filled.

When the shaft has been built up sufficiently remove the key and file off the excess metal to give a neat repair.

## TURNING THE AWKWARD GRUB SCREW

This tool for turning awkwardly-placed grub screws consists of a short **length of 9 mm diameter** mild steel bar with a hole drilled in the end to take a broken hexagonal key bronze-welded in position.

Take care not to overheat the key or it will become brittle and easily snap. Weld a handle on the bar to make it easy to turn, but beware of putting excess leverage on the handle and damaging the edges of the hexagonal socket.

The tool is shown here in use on a screw in a lock collar that holds a bearing in position behind a forage harvester.

## GASKET REPLACEMENT

Gaskets in engines seal surfaces that will not mate perfectly on their own. When two such surfaces are bolted together, the compressed gasket takes up small irregularities in the surfaces and makes a joint that will keep lubricant and water in and

If the seal between the two parts is difficult to break, tap the cover gently round the edges-with a soft hammer in the direction it comes off until the seal breaks. This plate was the back cover of a cylinder head water jacket and was well rusted on.

It is essential to clean the surfaces down to the bare metal. Use a scraper made out of an old file or steel rule to remove as much as possible of the old gasket and rust . . .

. . . and then finish off with a stiff wire brush to leave a smooth, even surface. If it is badly rust pitted, remove the studs and file down the surfaces until smooth and flat.

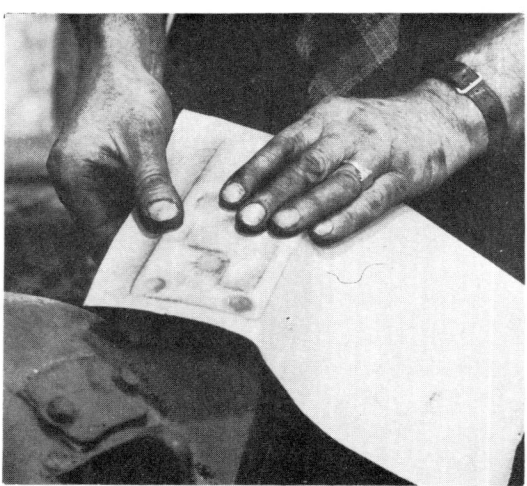

If the gasket you are making is particularly complex, it may be better to press the outline of the plate out with an oily finger and then cut round the mark with scissors.

dirt out. Where oil or water are likely to come in contact with the joint, gaskets are made of cork, oil-impregnated paper or rubber. Copper and asbestos, or asbestos alone are used in hot parts of the engine like the exhaust manifold or cylinder head.

Oil or water creeping out of an engine through a badly-fitted gasket means an expensive dismantling job. For engine overhauls or cylinder head gasket repairs, your dealer will supply a kit with all the gaskets required for the job. This is often cheaper than buying each gasket separately as required.

If no suitable gasket is available use gasket paper or card, obtainable from your dealer. Ordinary strong brown paper will do. Hold the paper firmly over the surface to be covered and, with a soft hammer, tap it gently round the

edges, bolt holes and oil-ways until the shape is cut out. Clean up the edges with a sharp knife or scissors.

When fitting a gasket that needs to be held in position while you hold an engine part, as with sump gaskets, a smear of light grease will stick the gasket in position while you bolt the part.

Use a tapered tool to line up the two parts and the gasket and make sure all the bolts are started in their threads before tightening down.

# MILKING MACHINE: FAULT FINDING

Only 25 per cent of the milking machines on British farms, MMB tests show, are working at optimum efficiency. This is due in part to faulty equipment and installation, but due mainly to faulty farm maintenance and operation.

Basic problem is a lack of knowledge of the components. A machine working sufficiently below the optimum to cause slow milking or teat damage could go unnoticed by the cowman, but most of the trouble is usually fairly obvious and should be put right by the operator.

By following the simple drill demonstrated here, it will seldom be necessary to call in an expert.

Most important is correct vacuum level. The pump should be large enough and the regulator working to give sufficient vacuum to maintain a constant level at the recommended pressure, usually about 380 mm of mercury, about 0.5 bar, both while milking and when units are changed.

Usually a steady vacuum shown on a gauge in good condition is sufficient, but a check against an accurate second gauge (1) is best. When units are removed during milking the gauge should not drop more than 25–50 mm, 0.03 to 0.06 bar, and should return to normal within five seconds.

Vacuum which is too low, and lack of reserve shown by a big drop and slow recovery when changing, can be due either to leaks or installation or poor pump capacity. Check pipeline components first, starting with stall taps and drain cocks (2). Usual trouble here is perished washers.

Worn rubbers on the units (3) are another obvious source of trouble. The leaks are often audible. Perished lid washers—including the one on the sanitary pail—should not be forgotten.

1

2

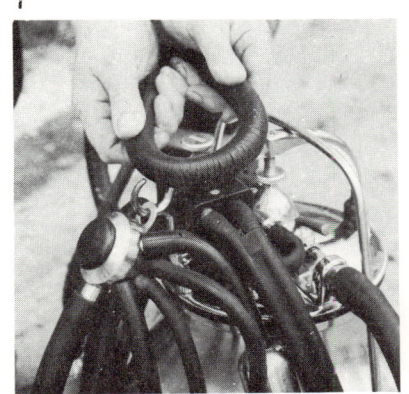

3

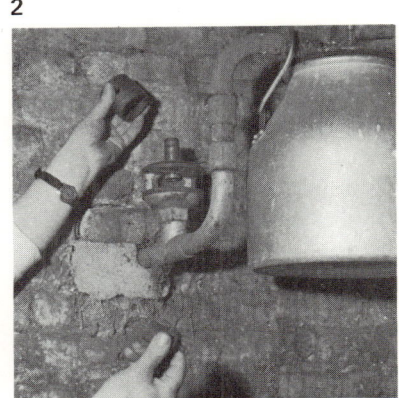

4

One of the most common faults on the pipeline comes from the vacuum regulator (4). Start the motor and listen as vacuum builds up. Air should begin to enter the regulator as working pressure is reached —not before or after. Dead weight types such as the one shown here must be level to work properly. Spring tension must be checked on the spring-operated type, but most important on both is the cleanliness of the valve and seating. These should be checked and cleaned every week.

If the vacuum is still too low the trouble must be in the vacuum pump. Assuming that the oil level is correct—it should be topped up weekly—the pump may not be running at the right speed (5). It should be running at 750 revs but in fact is doing only 500. Correct speed on the majority of machines is 1,400 rpm. Most usual trouble is a slack belt, which slips as the pressure builds up.

Adjust belt tension (6) to give no more than 12 mm of play midway between pump and motor. A common fault found by ADAS and MMB testers is that a pump too small for the number of units and length of pipeline is fitted. This often happens when components are bought second-hand.

When everything else has been checked, the pulsation rate can be adjusted by putting the thumb inside the teat cup and counting the number of times the liner collapses in a minute (7). The ideal is 50—60 a minute depending on the manufacturers' recommendation.

If all else fails call in the expert to check the pulsation ratio with a special instrument (8).

5

6

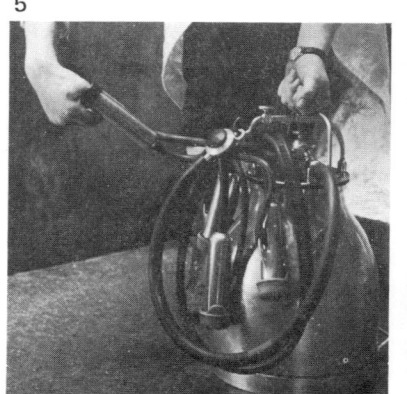

7

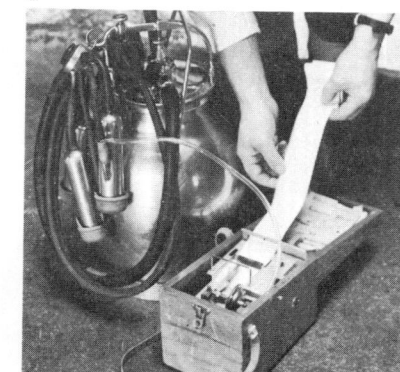

8

# INDEX